S0-BNH-122

WITHDRAWN

Mental Health and the Deaf:
Approaches and Prospects

Discrimination Prohibited

Title VI of the Civil Rights Act of 1964 states: "No person in the United States shall, on the ground of race, color, or national origin, be excluded from participation in, be denied the benefits of, or be subjected to discrimination under any program or activity receiving Federal financial assistance." Therefore, the training grants program of the Vocational Rehabilitation Administration, like every program or activity receiving financial assistance from the Department of Health, Education, and Welfare, must be operated in compliance with this law.

Mental Health and the Deaf:

Approaches and Prospects

Edited by

KENNETH Z. ALTSHULER, M.D.

JOHN D. RAINER, M.D.

A report of the National Conference on Mental Health Services for Deaf People, sponsored by the New York State Psychiatric Institute, Houston, Texas—February 14-17, 1968

362.42
N21m
101759
July 1977

This workshop was supported by VRA contract 67-54 from
the Rehabilitation Services Administration, Social and
Rehabilitation Service, U. S. Department of
Health, Education, and Welfare.

Published in 1969 by the U. S. Department of Health,
Education, and Welfare.
Library of Congress Catalog Card No.: 70-99881

Foreword

THESE PAGES bring to professional and lay workers for the deaf the fourth comprehensive document in the encompassing field of mental health for deaf people, specifically the report on the National Conference on Mental Health Services for Deaf People that was held in Houston, Texas, in 1968. As with the preceding publications, we are indebted to our colleagues from the beginning at the New York State Psychiatric Institute with whom this office has had the privilege of sharing in the pioneering of this basic work.

State vocational rehabilitation workers, persons in allied disciplines including psychology, social work, education, audiology, speech pathology, religion, and others will find in these pages much to stimulate their thinking and action. Improvements in diagnosis, in evaluation, in training, in counseling, and in supportive casework activity for deaf persons are logical, expected outcomes.

All readers will find encouragement and enrichment as they gain in these pages fresh views of the role of the psychiatrist in charting ground rules for human growth and development. The dramatic impact of psychiatry on the training of deaf children and youth here begins to come into focus. Practices that have permitted widespread functional illiteracy and extensive emotional involvement among a distinct population which is normally intelligent and basically stable come under more and more critical scrutiny through the objectivity and logic of the skilled mental health worker.

The Rehabilitation Services Administration deeply appreciates the splendid work of the planning committee in bringing to reality this important experience for voluntary workers for the deaf. We firmly believe that more and better services for deaf people will result.

JOSEPH HUNT
Commissioner

v

Table of Contents

APPENDIX

Introduction

THIS BOOK is the report of a conference which marked the end of one era and the beginning of a new one in the field of mental hygiene for the deaf. By its very format the meeting represented a coming of age, a cooperative and equal participation by all professional groups concerned with the deaf towards achieving a common aim. Psychologists and psychiatrists, educators and social workers, rehabilitation workers and the clergy joined forces with audiologists, leaders in the deaf community, and representatives of government agencies to pool their experiences, combine their suggestions, and reach a set of guidelines for a more coordinated approach to the mental health problems of the deaf.

Over the years, each of these groups had sensed increasingly its role in meeting the mental health needs of the deaf, and each had seen the need for the contributions and guidance of the other disciplines. The Planning Committee of the conference included representatives of each of the fields. Its work, and the conference itself were supported generously throughout by the Social and Rehabilitation Service (SRS); the steadfast interest of Miss Mary Switzer, Commissioner of SRS, and the consistently helpful prodding to do better by Dr. Boyce Williams, Chief of its Division of Communications Disorder warrant particular recognition. Members of the Planning Committee, themselves, labored long and well to develop an effective choice and distribution of persons contributing, the maximum of participation, and a productive conference overall; in particular Mrs. Elizabeth Wiggam, who acted as administrator of the conference, worked many months in polishing the local arrangements that made the meeting run smoothly and successfully. The assistance of Mr. Wally Newcomb and Miss Mima Cataldo in arranging and dealing with the many mechanical and administrative matters is gratefully acknowledged, as is the editorial assistance of Hella Freud Bernays in preparing this document.

The format of the meeting called for eight "resource papers" to be presented over the three morning sessions of the conference. In each paper, an individual prominent in his field was asked to summarize the situation in his own discipline. He was asked to do five things: first, to present something of the history of the involvement of his profession with mental health problems of the deaf; second, to describe the way in which mental health problems come to the attention of members of his professional discipline, what kinds of problems they have seen, in what context, and what they are expected to do about them; third, to describe with all frankness the successes and failures of his discipline in dealing with the mental health problems of the deaf; fourth, to give his suggestions, and those of other members of his profession whom he has consulted, for improvement of the services, including the all-important question of cooperation with the other disciplines represented.

Finally, each speaker was asked to start the ball rolling during the afternoon sessions, where groups would discuss the problems and propose concrete programs, including aspects of their organization, staffing requirements, and financing. Since the support of such programs usually falls within the province of the federal and state governments, the Committee included among the resource papers a review of federal programs under which financing might be obtained. Representatives of federal and state agencies were also asked to sprinkle themselves among the various discussion groups so as to answer questions of procedure and to clarify problems of policy.

Of course, each discipline has its own language, is confronted with somewhat different types of problems, and was expected to have its own emphasis regarding the types of solutions offered. It was not the intent nor the task of the conference to alter for any group its own particular form of service to the deaf, but rather to help all to define the common problems of human growth and development and the ways each professional discipline could best learn from and help the others.

Accordingly, the core of each of the afternoon discussion groups consisted of ten or fifteen representatives of one particular discipline—social work, rehabilitation services, education, religion, or psychology. With their leaders and recorders they met each afternoon for frank and pertinent consideration of the problems presented, their implications and solutions. They were expected to criticize and amplify the material presented in the resource papers—advance copies of which were distributed to the chairman of each group—and then go on to make their specific proposals. To help their deliberations, resource personnel were added to the discussion groups from disciplines not represented separately at the conference. For example, each discussion group had one or two government people, as noted earlier, and a similar number of psychiatrists to make available their particular skills and knowledge. Most of the latter specialists had attended the landmark workshop for psychiatrists held in New York the year before, where particular psychiatric problems related to deafness were discussed at length among the profession for the first time.* Each group also included directors

---

* National Conference of Psychiatrists Working in the Field of Deafness, New York City, April 7-8, 1967.
See Rainer, J. D. and Altshuler, K. Z. (eds.), Psychiatry and the Deaf. Proceedings of the National Conference of Psychiatrists Working in the Field of Deafness, U.S. Dept. of Health, Education, and Welfare, 1968.

of training programs, audiologists, members of the deaf community, and interpreters.

The recorders and chairmen carefully summarized the results of each group's discussions and presented them for plenary review on the final morning. The resource papers and the proposals of the discussion groups, refined for publication, constitute the body of this document.

Some of the highlights of these proceedings deserve mention here so that the reader will give them his careful attention. Williams sets the stage for the topic of this book by his inspiring but exacting keynote address; the editors then outline the psychiatric basis for the subsequent discussions and describe the prototype mental health program in New York State. Brown's psychological approach based on behavior modification through the environment is followed by Burke's detailed and pragmatic blueprint as seen from the vantage point of the rehabilitation counselor. Galloway provides a sensitive and most illuminating report on mental health as seen by the deaf person himself. A frank discussion of social work by Hurwitz surveys the present situation and makes penetrating suggestions for the future. McClure writes from long experience on the problems and frustrations of educators and deaf students. Msgr. Hourihan defines clearly and with authority the role of religion in the contemporary synthesis, and Krug relates with great specificity the relationship between audiology and the audiologist to mental health. A special check mark must be placed before Rosenstein's essential chapter on government funding, an indispensable and inclusive reference guide to the wide range of grant moneys available to state, local and community agencies prepared to work in this field. A future conference, perhaps one of state commissioners of education and mental health and rehabilitation, could very well be called to discuss and implement the challenges presented by this chapter. Finally, the five reports of the workshop sections supplementing these chapters, indicating the urgent needs, and offering concrete suggestions, will repay careful study.

There were some less tangible aspects of the meeting which should not be forgotten. The spirit of general and informal interdisciplinary communication was apparent to everyone; new friendships were made, and respect for each other's work strengthened. In a critical and self-critical approach, there was no whitewashing, but sincere and earnest searching for improvement. It was especially important to see the frank exchange of ideas and feelings between the deaf and hearing participants. And in the process of involvement with questions of mental health for the deaf, there emerged from the conference a practical feeling for the concept of mental health in general, something which psychiatrists, psychologists and social scientists have long tried to define.

The immediate value of this conference, and the enthusiasm generated as participants formed closer personal relationships, learned from each other, clarified their views, and went off to spark new programs, was unquestionable. Its enduring worth will become measurable only in the future by the caliber of work, the level of state and regional involvement, and the qualitative and quantitative improvement of interdisciplinary cooperation in mental health care for the deaf.

KENNETH Z. ALTSHULER, M.D.
JOHN D. RAINER, M.D.
Editors

KEYNOTE ADDRESS

Journey into Mental Health

BOYCE R. WILLIAMS

This is an occasion to remember, for here we take another important step upward in the long climb to adequate mental health services for deaf people. Up to now our attention with regard to the deaf has been largely directed to the medical professional in mental health. We have labored long to find him, to excite his interest, and to prick his professional conscience. We have sought to develop ways of supporting his work, and then to expand and focus his impact upon his own profession and upon the other important disciplines that are or should be concerned about the circumstances of deaf people.

With the opening of this conference we move back to the nonmedical professional and to the voluntary field. In the latter case, I say "back" advisedly, for every important service has had its roots in the activities of voluntary workers. The psychiatric sphere of mental health work for deaf people is now sufficiently well established, in a small way, to maintain itself. It is possessed of enough inherent momentum to move into communities where voluntary and lay persons have prepared the ground. Hence, it appears timely to turn again, more forcefully, to these other resources, to kindle among them even more interest, and even more promotional and supportive activities.

And so at this conference, we launch a long-planned meeting to chart clearly the responsibility of the interested lay and nonmedical professional person in the mental health of deaf people. Out of the lectures and discussions of the next few days each of us will acquire a more definite concept of what his role should be to bring appropriate mental health opportunities within reach of every deaf person in the land.

Origins

A firm foundation for our work in the future may be developed from a review of the origins of the effective and ongoing public mental health work for deaf people in this country. It is well known that the entire movement was triggered by the activities of voluntary workers.

1

Over twenty years ago, a picture appeared in a publication for the deaf of a Christmas party given to the deaf patients in a large state mental hospital by the deaf members of the surrounding community. It led to estimates that as many as 50 such patients might be in that hospital. "Startling!" "Appalling!" was the response. Was this large number typical or unique? What kind of service were they receiving? Were rehabilitation concepts operating? What were the economic aspects of the situation, the cost to the community of having these people vegetating instead of being helped and restored to society? These and many other questions were raised. But they were not answered easily, if at all. That voluntary workers' Christmas party thus lit the beacon to brighten a long journey toward the provision of better mental health services for the deaf.

Dean Richard Phillips of Gallaudet, at that time a colleague in vocational rehabilitation under state auspices, shortly thereafter carried out a rough survey of the mental hospitals in his state. He uncovered a relatively large number of patients with severe hearing impairment. Some time later, at the American Psychological Association meeting in 1952, Edna Levine of New York University reacted vigorously to a detailing of this information and its implications. An active but unproductive search for an interested psychiatrist ensued, until Franz Kallmann appeared at a social gathering of mental health workers. After a series of meetings and communications, a grant to the New York State Psychiatric Institute launched the first and pioneering program in the field of mental health services for the deaf. The program has grown, matured, and become permanent, and is the sponsor of this conference.

A detailed account of how Dr. Kallmann marshalled the staff who are today providing creative and inspiring leadership in serving the mental health needs of deaf people would be most interesting, I am sure. It is enough for our present purposes, however, to note that Dr. Kallmann quickly recognized the serious need to develop close and strong relations with the deaf community of New York State. Accordingly, in 1958, he held a meeting of deaf leaders of the deaf to orient them to the purposes of his work and to enlist their active support.

That meeting accomplished its purposes. More important to us at the moment is the fact that it was the springboard for our current conference. The Reverend Canon William Lange and others pressed for information about how they, as lay persons, could become more effective members of the mental health team for deaf people, and Dr. Kallmann agreed that he and his staff could provide the necessary training and direction. From then it proceeded gradually to the present, when we are about to take another long stride in the journey into mental health for our deaf fellowmen.

The fact that ten years have passed since Reverend Lange's question is revealing. The time has not been wasted. The ten-year interval emphasizes that where a great void in social service exists, activities such as these cannot be undertaken without long preparation. Urgency of the need is not the sole influencing factor. Community readiness, the extent of resources, and many other intangibles must be reconciled initially. We regret these unavoidable delays, and we are deeply grateful that at last we are on the way. Our indebtedness is total, to the late Franz Kallmann, to John Rainer, to Kenneth Altshuler, and to their associates, for their faith in deaf people, their steadfastness, their complete commitment, as well as for their many other substantive and endearing qualities.

By-products

Unexpected by-products of research are not uncommon. Such by-products sometimes prove to have great impact, to bring knowledge, comfort, and advantage to a degree beyond the scope of the originally intended study. Almost invariably they are very welcome. Such is the case in our research into the extent, care, and treatment of deaf persons with mental and emotional disorders.

Our initial hopes had been that scientific study of deaf people in mental hospitals would lead to the establishment of the principle that most deaf patients can be properly served only by professionals who are knowledgeable about deafness and who are skilled in receiving and sending manually. In other words, diagnosis of a deaf person would certainly be more accurate, complete, and helpful when it is made by a doctor who is able to communicate readily with his deaf patient. The frequency of improper diagnosis, with its shocking sequelae, should diminish in proportion to the availability of such doctors. Communication, the vital tool of counseling and therapy, is not really taking place unless an easy exchange of thinking exists. For deaf patients, such counseling and therapy come alive as a healing force in direct ratio to the doctor's ability to communicate freely with them.

Much has been accomplished in the few years since study in depth of this extraordinarily complex population has been pursued. In this we take great pride. We also find deep satisfaction in the fact that our persistence—to the point of nuisance in the beginning—has been fully justified.

Our greatest satisfaction may well be found in accomplishments beyond these immediate horizons. We have only begun to glimpse the potential of psychiatry as an influence on tradition-bound, empiric, but perhaps unrealistic practices in the training of deaf children and youth. A profession exhaustively trained to inquire into failure and to probe deeply for reasons certainly should find fertile fields in the widespread functional illiteracy of deaf people, in their social isolation among millions, in their emotional immaturity, despite years of training, and in their cultural poverty in the midst of a great society.

Even now, with only these few years of special attention, we begin to see a shifting of the rigid practices of a hundred years and more. We see, too, a commencement in sorting out of fact from wish, and an exciting rebirth of inquiry in our special schools, where the complete answers must eventually be found. In the light of this progress, it is reasonable to assume that with the increasing influence of psychiatry and its supporting disciplines, necessary changes in those basic practices that have produced generations of sharply underachieving deaf persons will be generally recognized, and remedial action correspondingly accelerated.

We are refreshed again and again as we watch the inquiring mind of the scientist at work with a deaf group. That albatross of deaf people, the rampant paternalism that degrades, imprisons, stifles, and defeats at every turn, has met its master. Psychiatrists, in general, feel no need to generate a false set of value standards by which to evaluate their patients. Accordingly, they measure deaf people by the same standards of performance as they do their hearing peers. The implications of such an attitude are far-reaching, and extend to every aspect of human behavior and adjustment.

The lavish praise, for example, that a deaf child frequently receives for classroom performance that is actually far below his true abilities, should surely give way to wiser patterns of rewards and motivation, under the expanding influence of our researchers in mental health. The deaf individual's sense of accomplishment should become correspondingly more realistic, his inner drive for self-improvement should be nurtured, and his capacity for self-evaluation heightened.

The deep social, psychological, and economic damage done to the value standards of so many deaf persons, in the name of opportunity, as they are propelled through educational experiences that are in serious conflict with their individual characteristics will diminish as research findings in mental health light the way to more appropriate choices.

Happily, the parents, too, will receive the attention they deserve, and their deaf children should benefit immeasurably. The conflict in claims unsupported by research, through which parents of deaf children have had to pick their way only to end up confused and frequently embittered should yield to findings which are even now becoming apparent. Earlier and more realistic language training in the home is an extraordinarily exciting prospect which might derive from the work of our researchers in mental health.

Thus, we can anticipate more and more realism, stability, and purposefulness in the whole structure of services for deaf people, as our relatively new professional colleagues spread their influence through compelling logic based on scientific study. Few expected at the outset that so much penetration into the core problems in deafness and so much revelation of what can and should be done in the family circle, in training, and in employment, would flow from the disciplined applications of workers in the mental health field. In hindsight, we can readily agree that we should have expected it, for the effects of mental health and illness are tremendous. With our first efforts crowned with success, we can demand a great deal more.

This "great deal more" is our beacon for the future. To repeat, scarcely ten years have passed since this vital work was begun. The next ten years promise to be still more exciting and rewarding. Our journey into mental health along the paths of self-respect, security, and personal satisfaction which deaf people seek, will be quicker, smoother, and shorter because of the work you are about to start at this conference. I urge you to continue it thereafter in response to your community needs at home.

The Development of
Mental Health Resources for the Deaf

JOHN D. RAINER

HISTORICALLY, it was the field of special education that first claimed the time and energy of those concerned with the welfare of the deaf. The ignorant and superstitious attitudes of medieval times gave way to the work of the early teachers, first private and then public. For well over a century the schools for the deaf in this country have been tackling, with increasing success, as well as with praiseworthy self-criticism, the difficult problems in the educational field. In the present century, psychologists at first became involved with problems of teaching, that is, with methods and results, measurements and systems. The recent formation of the National Advisory Committee on Education of the Deaf, the publication of the Babbidge report,[1] and the 1967 Colorado Springs conference,[2] mark the culmination of continued efforts to improve instructional facilities and methods.

Interest in the emotional welfare of the deaf was first shown in the schools, as educators began to think about individualizing instructional approaches to meet students' needs and to be concerned for the development of character in deaf students. The difficulties inherent in the whole field of working with the deaf, unfortunately, had tended to isolate the relatively few people in each professional discipline, and the mental health problems of the students in the schools were left to teachers and educators. These did as well as they could but found they had few people in other disciplines with whom to consult. Specialists willing to learn about the deaf and give of their time and interest to this particular field were few in number. It was the rare school that established paths of communication with psychologists, psychiatrists, social workers, or pastoral counselors.

If it was the school that was saddled with most of the emotional problems of the young deaf person, it was the vocational rehabilitation agencies that had these problems dumped into their laps once the deaf

7

person had left the educational field. The ordinary psychiatric and social work agencies very seldom saw deaf people and for the most part were helpless when they did. Those among the deaf who had psychiatric problems serious enough to warrant admission to a mental hospital could usually not get special care and attention. Very often they merely remained in the hospital for long periods of time without proper diagnosis or management.

In other fields, special attention has been given for a considerable time to the religious needs of the various faiths among the deaf community. A number of religious groups have worked together with the deaf themselves to organize not only church services, but also recreational facilities and a certain degree of personalized guidance for both the deaf adolescent and adult. Again, however, the cooperation that is needed between the clergy and the mental health professions if their services are to be of maximum usefulness was lacking. The largest gap to be bridged was probably in the field of social work. With a few notable exceptions, this important area of personal services was not available to many deaf youngsters and to most deaf adults. Audiologists, although they were aware of the emotional concomitants of deafness, had to concentrate on the speech and hearing aspects of the problem. The deaf community itself through its organizations helped a great deal to foster a sense of comradeship, and provided opportunities for social contact and leadership among the deaf. But it, too, operated in a relative vacuum when it came to a concerted attack upon the more serious mental health needs of the group.

This situation (perhaps somewhat exaggerated and with considerable geographic variation, of course) obviously could not continue indefinitely. During the past ten to fifteen years notable beginnings of a better professional approach to the problem have been made. The impetus for these beginnings came from all the disciplines I have mentioned. Today's conference is one culmination of a process that began over twelve years ago. At that time two of the professions, rehabilitation and psychology, realizing the need for a coordinated attack on the problem, got together and approached our psychiatric group and encouraged the organization of research and comprehensive services of a mental health nature for the deaf. Dr. Edna Levine, long associated with the study of the psychological problems of the deaf and officials of the then Office of Vocational Rehabilitation, (Miss Mary Switzer, the late Dr. Donald Dabelstein, and Dr. Boyce R. Williams) made contact at that time with Dr. Franz Kallmann, world-respected psychiatric researcher and clinician. Thus the mental health project for the deaf in New York State began. Dr. Altshuler, who is to follow me on the platform, will describe to you at greater length the development of our program in New York State.

Here I would like to focus on the gathering together of the strands of the various disciplines and the at-first hesitant, later more formalized, and today fully recognized cooperation between them. On the first advisory council of the mental health project in New York there were representatives of psychiatry in the person of the Commissioner of Mental Hygiene, and the Director and Assistant Director of the New York State Psychiatric Institute. There were representatives of psychology in the persons of two Columbia University professors of psychology. There were representatives of education, including the president of Gallaudet College and leaders in important schools and school systems for the deaf. There were representatives of religion. There was a famous otologist, there was representation of the field of rehabilitation in the person of New York State's Assistant Commissioner for Vocational Rehabilitation and finally, there was representation of the deaf community.

Every discipline represented here today, with the exception of social work, was represented in the early advisory council of the New York State mental health project. This, however, was only the beginning, at first a token beginning, later on a more dynamic progression from research and plans, to actual cooperation. In that program it turned out that there were still a good number of rough edges, of interdisciplinary rivalries, of problems and methods of cooperation to be worked out. Many discussions were held at national rehabilitation conferences, as well as with educators, with leaders of the deaf community, and with state rehabilitation directors. Members of our group were represented at national workshops for educators, for rehabilitation workers, for leaders of the deaf, for audiologists, at a workshop for social workers four years ago, and recently at a number of workshops run by various religious denominations.

Eventually members of the various groups began to cooperate in the search for guidelines for evaluation, and for sources of referral for guidance. Schools for the deaf began to hire psychologists, social workers and psychiatric consultants; religious leaders began to work closely with the mental health professions; rehabilitation agencies and psychiatrists began more and more to find ways of working hand in hand rather than asking the others to do the job alone. Increasing and much appreciated support from government agencies under the Department of Health, Education, and Welfare, created an atmosphere in which it became possible to recruit the former "outsider," that is, the professional who was not raised in the field of the deaf but who came into it with his specialized training and his equipment, with a fresh attitude and with a lack of preconception and prejudice. Training centers specifically represented in today's conference were established in various parts of the country.

I have spoken elsewhere of the growing concern of *psychiatry* with the deaf. The surprising neglect by the psychiatric profession of a field so obviously rich in theoretical and practical issues has come to an end. Last April the New York State Psychiatric Institute, in cooperation with the training center at New York University, conducted a workshop at which 35 psychiatrists from all over the country met to pool their experiences. Some were consultants to schools for the deaf, some were consultants to state hospitals, some had begun small projects for the deaf within hospitals. We were able to show them what we had done in New York State and they described to us their experiences in other parts of the country. Finally, the developments and the philosophy I have outlined have brought us here to Houston to do exactly what we have said must be done, namely, establish guidelines for dealing with the mental health problems of the deaf which can be subscribed to and utilized by all the professions represented here today.

REFERENCES

1. Babbidge, H.: *Education of the Deaf.* Department of Health, Education, and Welfare, Washington, D. C., 1965.
2. Altshuler, K. Z. (ed.): *Education of the Deaf: The Challenge and the Charge.* Department of Health, Education, and Welfare, Washington, D. C., 1968.

Crucial Aspects of Mental Health and Mental Disorder in the Deaf

JOHN D. RAINER

FROM THE vantage point of a psychiatrist and of one who has been involved in the administration of a mental health program for the deaf for a number of years I would like to outline, from a theoretical and practical point of view, a few of the highlights regarding normal and pathological emotional development. This development is responsible for the fact that we are all here to discuss this matter in so specialized a context. From a theoretical point of view, the problems which are seen by parents, teachers, employers, and others who come into contact with any individual stem from certain difficulties in the development of what we know as the ego, that is, the executive function of the mind, the function that perceives, selects, regulates, and communicates. The ego adapts the individual to his environment. In the development of this aspect of the personality, the infant normally progresses from the new-born's utter dependence on maternal care to the young adult's emotional and material self-reliance. At first the infant and the mother are as one. Gradually, the child makes his needs known and begins to recognize the mother as separate from himself, able to grant satisfactions or withhold them. He learns how to relate to his parents by trial and error, reward and admonition. As he grows up, he can use what he has learned with his parents in his dealings with other people. However if the pathway of communication between mother and child is lacking in the earliest years, a number of things can go wrong in this pattern.

First of all, the very young child can feel rejected, left out, and abandoned. In the hearing child with no communication barrier, both the anxiety and the depression have been described which such early maternal deprivation can cause. There is some question, however, whether in the deaf child the quality of the early relationship with parents ordinarily leads to depression or whether the anxiety aspect of this development is paramount. Secondly, without communication, the

11

growing child has no outlet for his impulsive needs and restlessness, so that he may behave destructively, have temper tantrums, and further alienate the parents. In the third place, the important process of learning how to relate to the parents, with all of its trials and tribulations, is necessary to develop a social sense, that is, a feeling for others. If this process is shut out by communication isolation in the early years, a child may grow up with severe deficiency in the area of empathic relationships.

Thus, in the early context of social communication with the parents, a great many of the later problems develop. There are other undesirable effects of the early warp in the ego that may come about through the communication lag caused by deafness. The development of conscience, the ability to handle power and strength, as well as the formation of a proper sense of identity is a direct consequence of the child's relationship to the family, to the father and to the mother. The emotional aspects of this relationship have probably been given less attention than questions of language and thinking, but they may be even more important. While some people have pointed out that thought processes—logical thought and adaptation—may develop without verbal language, without the usual kind of language the hearing child acquires,[1] the effect of communication isolation on personality development may be far-reaching, indeed.

The basic psychodynamic processes as I have just outlined them represent our distillation of over a decade of close work, study, and observation on deaf children, adolescents, and adults. Adverse results of the developmental gaps may be experienced first by the parents of young deaf children, frustrated in their child-rearing attempts. The more acute feelings of not belonging, of futile striving, of isolation, begin to appear in the deaf students at the schools. Teachers and educators are faced by them at the time the children have the first opportunity to contact persons outside the family. Sometimes as puberty begins, these children appear quite hopeless. Among the derivatives of these problems which we noticed in the schools have been poor academic performance, disciplinary problems, temper tantrums, hyperactivity, stealing, and sexual misbehavior. Even more striking have been a lack of group cohesiveness, even among adolescents, as well as a social and psychosexual immaturity. The complicated nuances of social and sexual mores, of rules and roles in dating behavior, and of mutual responsibilities in this field tend to be misconstrued and vaguely defined.

In cases of early brain damage or the rare instance of childhood schizophrenia, the usual symptoms are often mingled with a particular form of impulsiveness and acting out. Many forms of primary behavior disorder pose serious problems to classroom functioning and educational success.

Finally, in the adult deaf, besides the severe psychotic problems seen in the mental hospitals, these same developmental problems often result in marital and family difficulties, in impulsive behavior and inadequate personality, and occasionally in a picture which we have called "primitive personality," with severe deficiencies in psychological growth and maturation. There are many forms of social maladjustment, including cases of poorly structured antisocial behavior, and certain forms of impulsive, unruly, and often bizarre behavior. Drug addiction and alcoholism, while present among the deaf, seem to be less frequent than among the hearing population. Severe depression and the more structured forms of neurosis are also not found too often. Schizophrenia seems to occur in about the same frequency as it does in a similarly studied hearing group, but the symptoms are often difficult to establish by persons unfamiliar with the language patterns of the deaf.

So much for some of the theoretical framework and its consequences. From a practical point of view, we, as psychiatrists, realized from the outset but proved to ourselves even more fully as we went on, that our therapeutic program could not be complete without continuous collaboration with all of the nonpsychiatric professions that are represented here today. Since so many of the emotional problems of the deaf are problems of relationship to family, to society, to friend, to employer, we find that therapy involves patience, understanding, and concern with the entire environment of the deaf individual. Prevention requires attention to interactions on the family and school level, and rehabilitation means contact with all groups in the community prepared, able, and willing to offer their assistance. No one of our groups can do it alone, we all need to work together, we all need the help that each of us can offer.

REFERENCES

1. Furth, H. G.: *Thinking Without Language*. The Free Press, New York, 1966.

The New York State Program
of Mental Health Services for the Deaf

KENNETH Z. ALTSHULER

NEW YORK STATE since 1955 has pioneered in providing mental health services for the deaf. At that time the late Dr. Franz Kallmann commenced a Vocational Rehabilitation Administration-sponsored study designed to gather normative data on the deaf population of the state and to develop a body of psychiatric knowledge and experience that would be applicable to this special group. Dr. John Rainer and I had the privilege of being associated with Dr. Kallmann from the beginning, and have tried to continue and expand his work.

The original project included a pilot outpatient clinic and regular surveys of deaf patients hospitalized for mental illness throughout the state. To provide a backdrop of what it meant to be deaf—against which to view the psychiatric deaf patient—studies were made of 300 normal deaf individuals and their families, and of such special groups as deaf criminals, achievers, and twins.[1] A second program started in 1963 established a special inpatient treatment ward for deaf patients—now a permanent part of the state's mental hygiene department—and broadened the outpatient services.[2] Our third and continuing effort is an attempt to make the range of services truly comprehensive; it reaches into a school for the deaf for early diagnosis and prevention, and extends assistance to the deaf patient as he re-enters the community after hospitalization.

In this presentation I shall describe the organization of the overall program as it now stands and try to highlight its strengths and weaknesses. As the only one of its kind, it may well be useful as a model for other states, but the model may have to be altered in accord with differing population densities and types of needs, as well as to fill remaining gaps and to strengthen continuing weak spots.

Organization and Staffing of the Program

The heart of the New York State program is the special inpatient unit for the deaf. Located at Rockland State Hospital, this unit is under the administrative purview of the State Department of Mental Hygiene and the Director of the Hospital (see Fig. 1). The hospital is situated in a rural setting some 20 miles from the city, and holds about 7,000 patients from the New York City area. The ward itself, an active treatment unit primarily for acute patients, may serve up to 30 patients at a time (15 male and 15 female), referred from anywhere in the state. Provision is also made to rotate more chronic patients from our distant state hospitals for a trial of treatment, when the number of acute patients does not fill the census. Dr. Rainer and I, working out of the Psychiatric Institute in New York City—the state hospital devoted primarily to research and training, and an integral part of Columbia University—provide psychiatric supervision for the unit and other parts of the program, and we in turn are under the administrative direction of the Director of the Institute, as shown in the figure. The unit provides intensive inpatient treatment, including individual and group therapy, occupational therapy, pre-vocational evaluation, and pharmacotherapy or electroshock treatment in cases where it is necessary.

The outpatient department is housed in the New York State Psychiatric Institute located in New York City, a more accessible location than Rockland for people living and working in the city. It is staffed by the same professional personnel as the inpatient unit and serves deaf patients from all walks of life and with all degrees of disability, including those patients formerly hospitalized but now on convalescent care. Since its doors were opened in 1955, some 418 patients have been evaluated and treated. That this figure represents better than 2½ percent of the entire adult deaf population of the state clearly attests to the need for such a clinic, and we have no reason to assume that this kind of need is limited to New Yorkers alone.

The organization described up to this point is supported directly by the state. The school and community programs (see below) are presently funded by a grant from the Social and Rehabilitation Service; we hope that the broken lines in the figure may soon be made solid as these aspects, too, become at least partially incorporated into the permanent services of the state.

The second figure (Fig. 2) illustrates the staffing arrangements of the program. As already noted, Dr. Rainer and I are responsible for its overall functioning. We each devote a total of about one-half of our working week to the inpatient or outpatient departments, the school, or the community services. The professional staff of the ward do double duty, commuting to the city to man the outpatient clinic on the two days a week that it is open. The social worker and part-time rehabilitation counselor also serve in both departments and are heavily involved in maintaining an effective community program. Another psychiatrist, working with the school's mental health team of a social worker and a psychologist, is primarily charged with the preventive aspect of work at the school. Actually the organization is not so rigid as the outline, and anyone will pitch in wherever he is needed.

Functions of the Program

Now, what do we do with all this manpower and building space? The inpatient and outpatient units function as would be expected of any mental health treatment center. Patients who enter are evaluated by psychological testing and psychiatric interviews. Background data and information on past history and level of function are collated. These data are discussed in regular staff conferences where an appropriate treatment plan is drawn for the patient, and then implemented. All of this is more time-consuming for the deaf than it is for the hearing and requires a larger staff-to-patient ratio. Often it is unusually difficult to distil out of a clinical picture the extent of illness, the effects of deafness, the contribution of inexperience or distorted experience, and the pre-morbid potential. Yet each of these factors must be weighed in order to be able to develop a reasonable treatment plan and goal for a given case. Add to this the fact that psychiatric illness may make further inroads on an already limited ability to communicate, and you will see why our first formulations take time and are always subject to being amended in the light of further observation—at the regular reviewing conferences.

The treatment emphasis varies with the case. There may be a primary emphasis on medication and concrete directive counseling. Or the approach may be weighted in favor of education or training in communication, sometimes in conjunction with group therapy. A few cases have warranted a trial at a modified psychoanalytic form of therapy. We are also not averse to calling in relatives when their help is needed or when their own distortions appear to impede the patient's progress.

Outpatients who come to us generally have at least passable living arrangements, home bases that may need to be modified but from which the person may reach out as he improves. Not so the inpatient. Often he has been hospitalized for years, or has few interested relatives or none at all. It was not uncommon for us to work many months with a patient, to find—as he finally became ready for discharge—that there was no one to receive him. "Interested" families suddenly evaporated, were pre-occupied with other matters, or had no facilities to care for or watch out for him. With the double handicap of deafness and mental illness even improved patients were frequently not yet ready to "go it alone" outside the hospital. We sometimes found that by the time an adequate placement could be arranged, a critical period had been missed and the patient would slide back or fail to improve further. The same difficulties obtained in getting patients into training programs: few places were eager to take our patients, and those discharged might wait too many months before training became available, for which they had been ready at the point of discharge.

It was for these reasons that the community program was commenced. We tied ourselves in with Fountain House, a nonprofit halfway house in New York City, which assists the ex-hospitalized patient. Patients live with roommates, usually hearing, in apartments secured by the agency, and they use the facilities of the main house as a training center. There are courses in personal adjustment training, opportunities to socialize, and prevocational training in clerical tasks and homemaking. Through connections with industry, patients may be placed in such activities as carwashing, or later, in stores or factories where they can both work and earn. Even before they are ready for discharge, some of our patients are brought to Fountain House on a regular basis, to familiarize themselves with the physical plant, the social arrangements, and the available training.

Naturally, our staff must bear the brunt of responsibility for these deaf patients. Hospitalized cases are accompanied, at least on their first visits to Fountain House, and those living under the auspices of the House are visited frequently. Close follow-up is absolutely essential, especially in the early weeks following discharge; misunderstandings because of faulty communication can reach alarming proportions, and minor upsetting events have the potential to wreck months of treatment. For example, one recently discharged patient lost her purse and failed to show up for a job placement. She naively was unable, or forgot, to have the boss called. While she became panicky about the job and purse, the boss was ready to call the whole thing off. Our rehabilitation counselor, with some reassurance to both parties and a clear repetition of subway routes to the patient, was able to patch things up in this instance. Similar problems arise in the form of misunderstandings between roommates, as the residual symptoms of either one may wax or wane.

We have found the halfway house to be important as a bridge for the patient between the structured protection of life in the hospital ward and the openness of society at large. And the success of our patients there may partially be measured by the fact that the House now holds sign-language classes for hearing members, whose interest has been stimulated by their new relationships with the deaf.

A similar arrangement was worked out with the State Division of Vocational Rehabilitation. Our community program called for a full-time counselor to serve as liaison with the state division, working for both the division and the unit so as to expedite services to the patients and sustain that readiness for work that is often so difficult to achieve. Unfortunately, we were unable to find and recruit a well-trained person to fill that spot. As an alternative, which has begun to function almost as well, the D.V.R. sends its specialist in deafness to our ward for meetings once a month. As he so aptly puts it, we "make paper" early, so that cases are screened and opened well before the time of discharge, and arrangements for training are available for the patient to begin work on, as soon as he leaves the hospital.

Our preventive program grew out of still other considerations. Over the years the clinic had had a number of referrals from schools, for problems such as incorrigible behavior, underachievement, homosexuality, or simple maladjustment. Several other patients had been school dropouts, and our entire file of deaf criminals had had some evidence of troubled behavior during the school years. In several cases our feeling was that early diagnosis and treatment could have served a preventive function.

We had also had some preliminary experience in consulting at a school for the deaf. We had noted in the students a certain lack of mutual concern, a tendency towards irresponsibility which seemed more prolonged than in the hearing, and a curious kind of obedience to rules without a clear understanding of their reasonable bases. We felt that such obedience would have less restraining forces on impulses than a deeper understanding of why one should or should not do something— and, indeed, our adult cases typically have shown a good deal of impulsive behavior. We also thought that the school years would be a good time to present some idea of the genetic aspects of deafness, for while few of the adult population expressed a preference for deaf children, virtually none had shown any appreciation of the impact of genetic factors. Finally we were concerned with the difficulties parents had in raising a deaf child, in fitting him into the family, and in relating to him as his own needs required, rather than unwittingly using his silence as a screen on which to play out a range of their own family problems.

The school program was formulated to meet these several needs. Dr. Rainer or I visit one day a week to see individual cases for evaluation or treatment and to discuss students with teachers or cottage staff. The discussions include the school's mental health team and, we hope, are educational for the staff as well as being directed towards defining and solving the problems of the students. In addition we run a regular group meeting of adolescent students to encourage their understanding of themselves, each other, and the society of which they will soon form a part. Dr. M. Bruce Sarlin, the unnamed psychiatrist in Figure 2, is the other working member of this program. He sees individual students and runs another group. Of at least equal importance are the weekly meetings he has with groups of parents, one consisting of parents of young deaf children, and another of parents of older, adolescent students.

The parents of the younger children have greeted the meetings with an enthusiasm born of need. Their discussions are always lively, and sometimes touching. What to do, for example, in the face of explosive childhood rivalries, that arise when the deaf child requires a level of attention and patience that young hearing siblings cannot understand and may tolerate poorly. The parents of older children have been less easily involved. Having raised their children for many years, they have worked out ways of managing. Often they have a vested interest in maintaining the "correctness" of their views to keep out discomfiting questions—questions which may impinge on their perceptions of themselves as well as of their children. From discussions with them, however, has come a trenchant awareness that families often go through a depressing reappraisal at about the time the deaf child enters adolescence. The rapid expansion of social relationships and other pressures typical of this age often leave their deaf child far behind; physical coordination in games is suddenly no longer enough, and both parents and child must face limitations that were perhaps long denied in the hope that the educational process would lead to excellence in language and communication. We hope, by working with the parents of younger children, to temper hope with reality so that required compromises are arrived at gradually, earlier, and with less discomfort.

Dr. Sarlin has also recently started a special group for deaf parents of deaf children, a long-neglected but by no means unimportant segment of the parent population. The group has gotten off to a good start, but as yet it is too early in this experience to draw any inferences.

Evaluation of the Program: A Model for Other States

On the face of it, the overall program is a strong one. It emphasizes prevention, early diagnosis, intensive treatment, and then close follow-up and integration with other community agencies and the community at large. For the most part these emphases have yielded excellent results. I have already alluded to the proportion of the overall deaf population served by the clinic, and to the responses of parental groups at school. The group work with students has also moved well, and in addition some 22 children have been seen individually in the year since the school program was started. At least eight of these youngsters have been enabled to continue in school through the efforts of the psychiatrist and the mental health team.

The inpatient unit has served 75 deaf patients since its inception; 49 have been discharged and the vast majority are continuing to function in the community, although continuing to receive help as outpatients. Some of the results, such as our being able to discharge successfully after three months a patient who had been hospitalized elsewhere for 23 years, seem almost miraculous.

Yet certain weaknesses persist which must, along with other factors, be taken into account if the organization is to be useful as a model for other states. We have one part-time teacher to serve our 30 inpatients. This is grossly insufficient; an additional full-time person would be advisable. Many of the patients come with a rudimentary education at best and their further education is a difficult, frustrating task, and most time-consuming.

We have made steady progress in relations with community agencies, but in this area also, more remains to be done. The agencies need continuous persuasion to open these cases early, to expedite the transition to training programs at the optimum time, and especially to be educated to the fact that success in these cases cannot be measured as clearly as success in the face of a single handicap. More time and many trials may be required, goals must often be revised, and the whole concept of case closure may not even be applicable. In addition, "feeder" lines to and from the clinic and inpatient unit require continued strengthening so that all cases are not only reached, but reached early, and are enabled to continue or recommence functioning at whatever levels are possible.

Another unfortunate gap lies in the fact that neither in our program nor in any other is there a facility for intensive treatment of disturbed deaf children. We have seen a number of such youngsters, and, with the recent rubella epidemics, those requiring institutionalization and special help are likely to reach an even larger proportion.

Finally it should be noted that our program was designed for a densely populated area. In New York State, there are some sixteen million people—including roughly fifteen thousand adults who are deaf—and about half are clustered in the metropolitan section. While our clinic has been strained by the number of referrals, the small inpatient unit has not had this problem. This may be due to inadequate lines of referral from distant parts of the state, and a comparable, upstate unit may ultimately be necessary. Coupled with the scarcity of qualified and available personnel, however, the present experience may indicate the need for regional inpatient facilities working with outpatient departments that are organized by individual states, in areas of the country where the population is sparse.

This, then, is our current program in New York. Promising beginnings have been made elsewhere, especially in Chicago, in Boston, and in San Francisco, to mention but a few. We hope this framework and these experiences will be of help in your own efforts to imitate, innovate, and improve.

REFERENCES

1. Rainer, J. D., Altshuler, K. Z., Kallmann, F. J. and Deming, W. E. (eds.): *Family and Mental Health Problems in a Deaf Population.* New York State Psychiatric Institute, New York, 1963.
2. Rainer, J. D. and Altshuler, K. Z. (eds.): *Comprehensive Mental Health Services for the Deaf.* New York State Psychiatric Institute, New York, 1966.

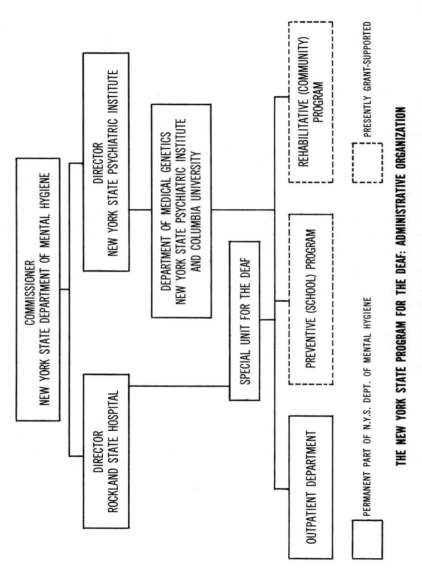

THE NEW YORK STATE PROGRAM FOR THE DEAF: ADMINISTRATIVE ORGANIZATION

Figure 1

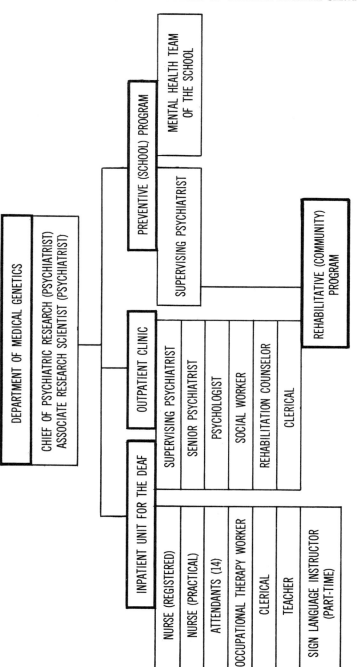

THE NEW YORK STATE PROGRAM FOR THE DEAF: STAFF ORGANIZATION

Figure 2

A Contemporary Psycho-Educational Approach to Mental Health and Deafness

DONALD W. BROWN

SEVERAL YEARS AGO I was privileged to see Anne Bancroft and Patty Duke portray Anne Sullivan and Helen Keller in *The Miracle Worker.* One scene from that play frequently comes to mind because it seemed to contain in microcosm all the essential components of a constructive approach to psychology and special education.

The scene was the confrontation of Miss Sullivan and Helen in the dining room of the Keller home. Helen was a little wild animal, one which had not been housebroken. She ate like an animal and she fought like one—but she met her match. Anne Sullivan had decided that Helen was going to eat at the table as a human being and she was determined that the child's eating with her hands, the grabbing, throwing, and stuffing the food, was going to stop. Helen resisted the change, to put it mildly. She had been king of the roost; everyone accepted her inappropriate, maladaptive behaviors as inevitable, because of her tragic dual handicap. Now she was to be dethroned—and dethroned she was! Anne Sullivan was convinced that Helen's disturbing behaviors were not due to her deafness or blindness, but that they had been learned in a particular environmental context and that they continued because they "paid off." As long as no one was disturbed about these behaviors or altered their reaction to them, they would not be changed.

But Miss Sullivan was disturbed! And in what Broadway critics called one of the most dramatic, tension-producing scenes ever literally to hit the stage, she and Helen battled with china, cutlery, and food. The audience were on the edge of their seats as tables were overturned, spoons were forced into Helen's hands and thrown away, and the two combatants, a disturbed teacher and a disturbing child, wrestled on the floor. The battle had begun at breakfast, and it was past noon when

25

Anne Sullivan emerged. But her statements to the startled mother: "She ate from her own plate" and "she folded her napkin," signaled the beginning of a really great transformation. Anne Sullivan had been confronted with a disturbing child and had become disturbed enough to do something about it—namely, change the behaviors which were disturbing.

It was this emphasis on *modifying behaviors* through the alteration of environmental expectations, requirements, and consequences that constitutes what we will call a contemporary psycho-educational approach to mental health and deafness. Our major thesis is that if we wish to understand, prevent, or eliminate what are often termed "mental health" problems in deaf individuals, we must view the causes and solutions as residing, not within the individual or in the nature of his handicap, but as stemming, generally, from environmental interactions.

Psychological Framework

Stated simply, psychology is the study of behavior. Its focus is on the acts and productions of individuals and groups, and on how behaviors of human beings are learned, maintained, modified, and eliminated. One tenet of the behavioral scientist is that B=f (P,E) where behavior (B) is a function (f) of or caused by, interactions of the person (P) and his environment (E). In much of psychology today, however, one component of this equation has frequently been emphasized at the expense of the other two. The *person* has been scrutinized, analyzed, and even vilified, as if he were a host organism within which dwelt the seed of all of his behaviors. The implication has been that if we could correct the attitudes, desires, and feelings of the person, we could eliminate, or at least minimize, maladjustment. A major criticism of this approach is that it blatantly presumes that *all* environments are normal, and that if Johnny is "out of step," it is primarily because of aberrations within him, not in the actions, reactions, teachings, and treatment he receives from others.

Because of this preoccupation with what are variously called the personality, attitudes, or "characteristics" of the individual *apart* from the environmental events impinging upon him, descriptive studies have been conducted in an attempt to arrive at inventories of attributes. To no group does this apply more than to the deaf members of our population. Throughout history the deaf individual has been accused of a host of liabilities. His profile, drawn up by well-intentioned members of the helping professions, has included: Mentally retarded—because of no language and consequently deficient in thought processes; concrete; dependent; conceptually deficient; educationally retarded; suspicious; isolated from general society; more prone to emotional disturbance than "normal" people.

These labels have resulted from formal and informal observations aimed at demonstrating that the company of people homogeneous for hearing impairment is homogeneous in respect to other traits as well.

In our scientific quest to identify and understand problems, we have unintentionally made some of the same errors as the bigot, who, in order to simplify his approach to life, must treat individuals in terms of imagined group-membership characteristics.

In recent years, however, voices have been raised to say, "Look around you. What situations are responsible for disturbing behaviors, or for the absence of necessary adaptive behaviors?" If environmental events are causing some deaf individuals to flounder in academic, social, and personal areas, then let us change these events and influences. An example of this more contemporary view that real or imagined deficiencies are not due to deafness *per se,* is found in the words of Levine:

> To label the deaf "concrete thinkers," whatever that might mean, is simply an evasion of the problem. If the deaf function at a lower level of conceptualization than their hearing fellows, it is logical to assume in the light of today's knowledge that education has not yet found the way to raise the level.[1]

This should not be viewed as an indictment of education. It is, rather, an assertion that since behaviors are learned, a deficiency can be prevented or overcome by appropriate instruction and consistent reaction to the individual's behavior.

What does all this have to do with mental health, deafness, and psychology? I suggest that what we refer to as mental health is a collection of behaviors which enable an individual to function appropriately, and thus acceptably, in average environments. The development of these behaviors can prevent so-called "maladjustment" and is accomplished by arranging and manipulating the environment. Conversely, maladaptive behaviors can also be *produced* and mistakenly attributed to the alteration of the person by deafness. If we search too long and too hard for underlying flaws *within* the individual, over which we have little or no control, we may miss seeing the influence and functional properties of external events which we can control. Let me illustrate how this viewpoint can affect our professional endeavors with deaf individuals. To do so let us return to the Helen Keller-Anne Sullivan relationship and consider three points which their interactions seem to reveal: naming the problem is not enough; disturbing behaviors are not inevitable and can be modified or eliminated; so-called "abnormal" behaviors may be normal reactions to abnormal situations. As we consider these points we shall endeavor to describe how a psychologist can contribute to maximizing the probability that a deaf individual will possess those behaviors which represent optimal "mental health."

Naming the Problem is not Enough

Anne Sullivan could have looked at Helen's behavior and said, "She is emotionally disturbed, and since I am a teacher of deaf-blind children, not of the emotionally disturbed, this is not the job for me." She could, after naming the problem, have longed for a special facility for all children whose problems had been given the same name, so that she could be left to work with deaf-blind children whose behaviors were like what she thought deaf-blind children's behaviors should be. But she was apparently less interested in "the name of the game" than in how to win the battle. Perhaps her thinking went something like this:

> Helen has learned a lot of behaviors which are holding her back; she has not learned any of the behaviors that are essential for survival and success. I am going to do something about it so I am afraid I do not have time to ask whether she is Strauss syndrome, rejected, aphasic, emotionally disturbed, mentally ill, retarded, or minimally brain damaged. I do not know that if I grouped all the brain-injured children together, or all the "culturally deprived" or all the understimulated or overstimulated children, I could do a better job. All I know is that Helen needs to learn to dress herself, feed herself, read, write, travel, follow directions, and become somebody. And I am the only one here who can do something about it. This is where Helen is. I don't like it! I am disturbed about it. I am going to move her a little further along.

Psychologists and special educators are beginning to say much the same thing. An avid interest in remediation is emerging in place of an undue concentration on diagnosis. Convinced, in this "era of the diagnostician," that labeling a problem does not correct it, many professionals are echoing Font's words:

> . . . if I were to make a recommendation to you as teachers of the deaf, who are concerned about the child who comes to you and does not "behave" as a deaf child, it would be to worry less about his diagnostic category and be more concerned about the number of ways that you might approach this child.[2]

But we still frequently see signs which imply that naming problem behaviors is equivalent to explaining or justifying them. It is almost as if, when given a diagnostic label, we sigh and say, "Oh, he is emotionally disturbed, no wonder he is not learning. Now *I* do not need to be so disturbed. If only someone had told me that earlier, I would not have worried about his temper tantrums, his perceptual difficulties, and his slow learning."

That psychologists have contributed to this attitude cannot be denied. Our concentration on causation, fixed limits of ability, and inferred internal dynamic status has implied that the "medical model" of searching for the cause before dealing with the "symptoms" should be applied to human behaviors as well as to physical illnesses. Proponents of a "psychological model" however, assert that inappropriate, or maladaptive behaviors are significant in and of themselves and are *learned* according to the same principles that account for the learning of adaptive behaviors.[3] Maladaptive behavior is not seen as qualitatively different from what is arbitrarily defined as normal behavior.

A psychologist adopting this frame of reference thus attempts to establish those environmental conditions, *i.e.*, reactions of others, consequences of behavior, and presentation of stimuli, which will promote the development of desired behaviors and eliminate undesired ones. He will actively apply one of the slogans of the Peace Corps: "Stop looking for a cause . . . start an effect."

Disturbing Behaviors Are Not Inevitable and Can Be Modified

Rather than attempting to analyze an individual, psychologists who are committed to a behavioral approach to learning and mental health, are likely to ask three questions: (1) What behavior is maladaptive, *i.e.*, what behaviors should be decreased or increased? (2) What environmental contingencies currently support the subject's behavior (either by maintaining undesirable behavior or reducing the likelihood of his performing a more adaptive response)? (3) What environmental changes may be manipulated to alter the subject's behavior?

What such a focus can lead to is exemplified in the work of Meyerson, Kerr and Michael[4], who report on working with a nine-year old retarded girl. They were told that the child had never been known to walk in all the seven years she had been in the school for the retarded. When they asked why the girl did not walk, they were told that it was not unusual for severely retarded children to be unable to walk. When they asked how it was known that the child was retarded, one of the answers was, "Well, she doesn't walk. . . ." They began working with the girl for 15 to 20 minutes every day. To begin with, the two researchers placed the child in a standing position between them. If she moved even slightly toward one of the men, she was given a piece of candy. Gradually her reward was withheld until she had taken one full step, then two, and so on. At the end of nine hours of work, the girl was walking all over the building and the grounds. Now the walking became its own reward; it brought so many new experiences into the child's life that no further tangible reward or reinforcer was necessary. Prior to this the child had gotten everything she wanted without having to walk. Because her failing to walk was accepted as inevitable, her needs had been met without her having to walk. Like Anne Sullivan, the researchers changed the rules, and the child's behavior had also changed.

In another problem situation, like many facing special education today, Kerr[5] eliminated lack of attention and hyperactivity. Two girls diagnosed as brain-injured displayed gross hyperactivity in their classroom and did not attend to a task for longer than three to six minutes at a time. Kerr devised a simple task, folding 2 x 5 cards along a dotted line and placing each card in a container. During the first three sessions she used a common technique, that of urging continuation. Whenever the child's work began to lag, the experimenter would say, "Come on, you can do better than that." and approximately ten minutes of productive behavior was obtained. But this was giving teacher attention to exactly the behaviors that were not wanted. During the next three sessions, the experimenter gave some expression of approval whenever the desired behavior was displayed, and a full hour of work was obtained each time.

Similar "behavior modification" techniques have been employed to teach speech to autistic children[6], eliminate temper tantrums[7], reduce hyperactivity and inattentiveness[8, 9], and develop reading and arithmetic skills in retarded children.[10]

These are only a few illustrations of possible results when we change from asking why a child or adult cannot do such and such, to how we can teach and develop the desired behaviors.

So-called "Abnormal" Behaviors May Be Normal Reactions to Abnormal Situations

Anne Sullivan was obviously convinced that there was no necessity for Helen Keller to be completely untrained in socially acceptable, independent, self-help skills. It is doubtful, however, that she was surprised by Helen's maladaptive behaviors. She could see how Helen's family, understandably dismayed by the child's tragic dual handicap, was allowing Helen to obtain everything she wanted through her temper, wildness and disregard for others. In Hurwitz's terms[11], Helen was on her way to becoming a "Career Infant," not because she was deaf-blind, but because her environment was not providing clear information about which behaviors were appropriate and which were not.

With what must have been an intuitive understanding of one of the basic principles of learning, Anne Sullivan recognized that the most fundamental way to eliminate an unwanted kind of behavior from an organism's repertoire is to discontinue the effect the behavior has on the environment. She thus started by teaching Helen's parents, not Helen, how to foster the development of acceptable actions rather than the bizarre behaviors they were currently permitting. As Rhodes[12] recently suggested in his provocative discussion of "The Disturbing Child," Anne Sullivan became a teacher to Helen's living units, modifying not only the child but the crucial units which contained the child.

Helen was displaying the only behaviors she had learned in response to abnormal situations. As the situations were altered, so was her behavior. It is one of the contentions of this paper that many of the disturbing behaviors of some deaf children or adults are normal reactions to abnormal situations. We have not yet learned to teach some of the skills required for effective living in average environments, and an individual's deficiency in being able to respond adequately to many life situations can easily be viewed as deviance or disturbance. But, lack of training is even more handicapping than lack of hearing.

Some deaf children are still in "little-red-school-house" educational programs, where children with a wide range of age and achievement attend classes housed in a single room, are taught by one inexperienced teacher after another, and frequently experience drill in speech that is emphasized at the expense of systematic instruction in essential school and social skills.

The prevention of mental health problems, or inadequate functioning, obviously requires the elimination of procedures and programs which spawn failure rather than success, and frustration instead of motivation.

Psychologist's Changing Role

If the contributions of the science of behavior are to be applied to the habilitation and rehabilitation of deaf individuals, the psychologist's work cannot be peripheral to the educational, social, and vocational activities in which the deaf person is involved. The psychologist must work closely with all professionals in discovering and utilizing better methods of instruction and more effective ways of modifying behavior. From cataloging deficits and diagnosing disabilities, he must turn to suggesting practical techniques of remediation.

Assuming, as has been suggested, that there are many ways in which those of us who work with deaf individuals unintentionally establish and maintain maladaptive behaviors, the psychologist with his expanding knowledge of the principles of learning may be of greater benefit to us as a designer of instructional methods and materials than as a diagnostician or therapist. In the crucial, but generally neglected area of parent education, he may, by viewing parents as agents of training rather than objects of therapy, be able to learn and suggest ways in which parents can alter their own behaviors to bring about constructive changes in their children. And through his growing concern with the "technology of teaching," the psychologist who learns from and works with educators may help usher in the day when the art of teaching truly becomes the science of teaching.

REFERENCES

1. Levine, E. S.: Psychological testing and education: Some current concepts. In *Proceedings of the International Congress on Education of the Deaf*. Gallaudet College, Washington, D. C., 1963.

2. Font, J. F.: Aiding the schools toward a better diagnosis. In *A Handbook of Readings in Education of the Deaf and Postschool Implications*. (I. S. Fusfeld, ed.). Charles C. Thomas, Springfield, Ill., 1967.

3. Ullmann, L. P. and Krasner, L.: *Case Studies in Behavior Modification*. Holt, Rinehart & Winston, Inc., New York, 1965.

4. Myerson, L., Kerr, N. and Michael, J.: Behavior modification in rehabilitation. In *Readings in the Experimental Analysis of Child Behavior and Development*. (S. W. Bijou and D. M. Baer, ed.). Appleton-Century-Crofts, New York, 1968.

5. Kerr, N.: Applications of behavioristic techniques and field theoretical concepts in somato-psychology. Unpublished doctoral dissertation, University of Houston, 1962.

6. Hewett, F.: Teaching speech to an autistic child. *Amer. J. Orthopsychiat.*, 35: 927, 1965.

7. Williams, C. D.: The elimination of tantrum behavior by extinction procedures. *J. Abnorm. Soc. Psychology*, 59: 269, 1959.

8. Patterson, G. R.: An application of conditioning techniques to the control of a hyperactive child. In *Case Studies in Behavior Modification* (L. P. Ullmann and L. Krasner, eds.). Holt, Rinehart and Winston, New York, 1965.

9. Brown, D. W.: Operant conditioning of attending and verbal imitation of deaf children with deviant behaviors. Unpublished doctoral dissertation, University of Illinois, 1967.

10. Bijou, S. W.: Application of operant principles to the teaching of reading, writing and arithmetic to retarded children. *New Frontiers in Special Education*, Council of Exceptional Children, NEA, 1965.

11. Hurwitz, S.: Behavior patterns in the deaf. *Rehab. Record, 8:* 15, 1967.

12. Rhoades, W. C.: The disturbing child: A problem of ecological management. *Except. Child, 33:* 449, 1967.

Vocational Rehabilitation and Emerging Mental Health Service Needs of the Deaf

DOUGLAS BURKE

In discussing the relationships between vocational rehabilitation and mental health services for the deaf, certain presumptions should be clearly shared from the outset. First, other service agencies tend to refer deaf persons to the vocational rehabilitation counselor for further clarification of their needs. Such a counselor of the deaf, if he has warm rapport, is the one to whom a deaf person really turns when he is in need of services. Secondly, and most important, we are talking about mental health services specifically "for the deaf." In other words, guidelines based upon experiences with the hearing community, when applied to the mental health problems of the deaf, have only as much validity as tests based on hearing norms have when we are testing the deaf. It is important that we know what mental health services are available to the hearing public; but to meet the mental health needs of the deaf population we must select carefully from among them.

My own experience is based on the fact that I am a graduate of institutions for the deaf as well as a longtime active member of the deaf community. Eleven of my past twelve years in employment have been spent in counseling in one form or another. I have worked as a dormitory counselor, as a psychiatric group worker with emotionally disturbed children, and as a vocational rehabilitation counselor. In addition to a moderate amount of participation in sensitivity training and social vocational group counseling, I have served as interpreter in many therapy sessions with deaf clients, and participated in countless psychiatric staff conferences on deaf hospitalized patients.

33

THE VOCATIONAL REHABILITATION ROLE AND
MENTAL HEALTH SERVICES MANPOWER

There are a number of possible perspectives on the role of vocational rehabilitation in community mental health service centers. A mental health view is that vocational rehabilitation comes into the picture when the patient is ready to take on vocational responsibilities. The medical profession has a similar perspective. Adequate mental health services for the deaf, however, scarcely exist anywhere today and the vocational rehabilitation counselor has to be the prime mover for the development of such services in a given community. Vocational rehabilitation counselors can and should try to develop a comprehensive service plan of which mental health services are a part.

One way of approaching the problem would be to have existing community mental health service centers and those in the planning stage brought around to serving the deaf. The vocational rehabilitation counselor, because he is probably more aware of the problems of the deaf than any other service agency in the community, should be the one who initiates meetings with these centers for the purpose of bringing about adequate services.

This should not be too difficult to achieve. The prime obstacles are time and personnel trained to handle the mental and emotional problems of the deaf. Perhaps a registered interpreter for the deaf would have to serve as an intermediary. This would be at least a beginning, even though not a total answer.

Of course the manpower shortage in mental health services is not unique for the deaf. Budgeted positions for physicians and psychologists in county and state hospitals are nearly 25 percent unfilled, and for psychiatric nurses and social workers they are 20 percent unfilled. In contrast, only 4 percent of the non-professional jobs in the field remain vacant.

As Albee noted, "Even if all available jobs were filled, the staffing of public mental health hospitals would fall far short of the minimum standards for adequate care set by the American Psychiatric Association."[1] By these criteria, our hospitals are only 20 percent adequate in nursing staff and only 36 percent adequate in social workers. For physicians the adequacy is 45 percent (with heavy reliance on foreign internes and residents) and for psychologists 67 percent.

At our current rate of population increase, approximately three million persons a year, the country will have a population of about 250 million in fifteen years. Surveys based upon the current output of trained mental health personnel indicate that we shall fall still further behind in the supply of both psychiatrists and doctors in general.

Taking a maximum population of 500 thousand deaf adults, we should now have 27 trained psychiatrists as a minimum, while we would need about twice that number, or 54 for adequate services in the proposed ratio for the hearing population. Because of special problems related to the treatment of deaf patients, we probably need about 75 psychiatrists. How do we stand in terms of clinical psychologists, social workers, and psychiatric nurses for the deaf? These professionals must have specialized training and experience in communication and in the mental health problems of the deaf. Before a mental health program for the deaf can be developed for later implementation, this conference must first define and make clear the mental health problems that are of the greatest importance in the deaf community.

Finally, there is still an acute shortage of vocational rehabilitation counselors for the deaf, although the problem has been alleviated to some extent in the past decade. Considering how important the rehabilitation counseling profession is for the deaf, this scarcity alone would be sufficient reason for concern. There seems to be a trend for more and more of these special counselors to move into other related professional fields. This may be due to the dearth of personnel trained to work with the deaf in other areas, greater room for promotion, or better salaries, or still other reasons. The matter should be scrutinized, so that state agencies can retain their counselors of the deaf at least until they have a mental program off the ground.

MENTAL HEALTH FACILITIES AND SERVICES

For a truly comprehensive mental health service program the following services are considered vital: inpatient services, outpatient services, partial hospitalization, community services, diagnostic services, rehabilitation services, complete care and after-care services, training, research, and evaluation. As a first step towards these services, the vocational rehabilitation counselor would do well to try to obtain at least one psychiatrist or clinical psychologist in every major community (city) mental health service program in his state. Considering the manpower shortage, a counselor's persuasiveness might be enhanced if he would point out that about 10 percent of the population in this country suffers from hearing deficiencies and related psychological difficulties. The severity of problems related to hearing impairment is evident to most clinical psychiatrists and psychologists, if only by implication, and this should help the cause of obtaining a specialist for the hearing impaired, at least in major metropolitan communities.

The next step would be to have the specialist learn to communicate with the deaf or to utilize the assistance of what we might term a "psychiatric interpreter." Once a nucleus is established, the remainder of a program can be developed around the center, probably with the help of case-service funds. Eventually an appropriation to the mental health center program for service in this specialized area could be obtained.

Most major communities have a program that includes preventive, diagnostic, treatment, rehabilitative, and supportive mental health services, directed toward enabling the individual to continue or return to participation in family and community life. Below are listed some of the areas.

Emergency Services

Services here are aimed at crisis intervention and include emergency consultation services. An around-the-clock telephone service is available so that when a crisis arises individuals can receive consultation information and proper referral in mental health matters. The vocational rehabilitation counselor could have several competent interpreters and himself listed as available for these emergency situations. Unlike the physician, the counselor would not have to be on call frequently, for such occurrences are relatively infrequent among the deaf, and generally can be deferred to a regular working day.

The same suggestions apply to an around-the-clock, walk-in, service center. The deaf adult may have experienced a psychological crisis at a club meeting, or during a family conflict, or because of some frustration on the job. He may have a need to discuss this problem with the professional on duty, again requiring the aid of an interpreter.

Emergency Home Visit Services

In some communities emergency house calls are available, usually by psychiatric nurses. During these calls, the nurse may offer counseling or recommend a patient for voluntary hospital admission. Home visitors should have easy access to a list of qualified interpreters, if they themselves are unable to communicate with the deaf adult.

Suicide Prevention Services

While information about this aspect of psychiatric illness is hazy in most populations, suicide attempts do occur among deaf adults from time to time. Severe stress, depression, grief, or endless feelings of loneliness may be the factors involved. The vocational rehabilitation counselor could provide information on various aspects of these psychological crises and on the emergency services available to meet them. A special telephone number could be made available for emergency purposes.

Clinic or Diagnostic Services

Most major communities have mental health clinics situated in various parts of the city so that the patients receiving services can remain employed, carry on their school or housekeeping routines, and still keep a regular therapeutic schedule. Psychiatric outpatient treatment is offered in the form of psychotherapy, group therapy, family therapy, psychodrama, and the organic therapies, including electroconvulsive and drug therapy. Patients needing to be maintained on drugs on a long-term basis also report regularly to the clinic.

All these areas of service could be made available to the deaf. Instances where extensive psychotherapeutic communication is necessary would require that the deaf person commute to a clinic that agreed to serve all of the deaf in the particular locality. As the next best thing, the vocational rehabilitation counselor could organize groups of interpreters in various locations in the community to be on call whenever needed by the clinics. For the interpreters to do this kind of work would entail what might be called "out-service" training. The counselor could also urge that mental health clinics request funding to pay for interpreters and for their training. Even more important, the counselor should be sure that the adult deaf receive and understand information about these clinics and about the services they are prepared to render.

Residential Services

To return the patient more rapidly to his environment, partial hospitalization services are offered under this program. This means day-time, after-school, evening, and night or weekend services. Such outpatient services can be very helpful to deaf adults who are returning to live with families, to their employment situations, or even to their schools. At the same time, inpatients may also need such outside residences, training and employment situations as would enable them to gain experience by living or working or participating outside the hospital.

The vocational rehabilitation counselor can do much to help a deaf adult in any of these situations. With a working knowledge of the deaf community, he will be able to contact mature individuals in the community who would be willing to take on these inpatients during their temporary adjustment period. He would also be able to arrange evaluation and training programs for inpatients, including part-time residence with a deaf family or with a hearing family who had a knowledge of manual communication.

The counselor could arrange part-time job training and therapeutic programs for deaf adult outpatients residing in the community. He could also facilitate a deaf adult's integration with local organizations of the deaf, church groups, social clubs, or cultural groups. The counselor might establish a mental health volunteer program for deaf adults, supply them with in-service training, and find ways in which they can be helpful to the deaf mental patient who is on the road to recovery.

Home Psychiatric Services

These services, involving psychiatric services in the patient's home, foster home care, nursing home care, and group homes or halfway house care, are an alternative to full hospitalization for many patients. With the exception of the arrangement in New York, the adult deaf patient is usually the only one in a halfway house or nursing home setting. Deaf adults might do better if they remain in a therapeutic milieu, and psychiatric services in the patient's own home or foster home might be more easily geared to meet his recovery needs. In these situations the emphasis should be on adequate communication.

Public welfare might oppose the vocational rehabilitation counselor in his efforts to place the recovering patient in a foster home with deaf adults. If the patient would clearly benefit from such care, the counselor should summon all the powers-that-be to make it possible. It is most important that the psychiatrist or psychologist recommends this type of home placement and that the "foster adults" have been sufficiently screened and prepared for this type of responsibility.

Rehabilitation Services

Here the vocational rehabilitation counselor of the deaf should be very much at home, even with clients who have mental health problems. There are five major areas of services, dealing with educational, vocational, avocational, socialization, and recreational needs.

Most mental health facilities are able to offer some form of occupational therapy, manual arts therapy, industrial or work therapy, vocational counseling, vocational training, and education or remediation, recreational therapy, and job placement services follow-up. In these areas the vocational rehabilitation counselor can apply his talents directly. Hospitals no longer wait until a patient is completely recovered before exposing him to rehabilitation services. Patients are brought to the rehabilitation services program as soon as there is some indication that benefits will accrue. The patient may be just beginning to recover or he may even need these services to help him recover.

The rehabilitation counselor should bear in mind that the patient who receives rehabilitation services in the hospital setting still requires therapy. The situation is different from the raw exposure such a patient would receive in the competitive labor market or even in a moderately competitive sheltered workshop. While developing new emotional outlets in the rehabilitation program, the hospitalized deaf adult is bound to be extra sensitive to hints of rejection and to the disappointment and frustration that one is apt to receive socially on a new job, in training situations, or even in recreational activities. During this delicate adjustment period, the counselor for the deaf should take precautions to avoid premature exposure or overexposure to stress and strain in areas that are highly or ruthlessly competitive.

The counselor also must, on occasion, have a great deal of fortitude. Parents, service persons, and forceful leaders of the deaf in a given community will often voice concern about a deaf person who is hospitalized. Sometimes these people have only a scanty knowledge of mental illness and the problems encountered by the patient during his recovery. In addition, some extremely anxious patients may write letters to outsiders that can touch the heart of any sensitive person and move him to act for the patient's release. Recipients of such appeals may become active because they have known of other deaf individuals who, neglected because of inadequate facilities and services, have remained hospitalized indefinitely. They undoubtedly have the welfare of the deaf adult at heart. The counselor, with feelings of his own for these patients, would also like to see them recover completely. Yet, when a patient is not ready to stand the pressures and strains of independent living in the community, the counselor will find it necessary to prevent well-meaning individuals from rocking the patient's recovery boat. When the psychiatrist is unable to make this decision, due to his unfamiliarity with the problems of deafness and his lack of communication with the patient, he may rely a little more on the counselor than he normally would. This puts the counselor in a touchy situation in which he needs all his powers of perseverance and discrimination.

The rehabilitation counselor should not hesitate to encourage or establish a volunteer program to work with deaf patients. These deaf adults and service-oriented persons can and often do become regular "visiting friends" of the deaf patient and his therapeutic link with the fast-moving, competitive, and changing community outside.

There are other facilities such as homemaker services, university services to the community, public education services, sheltered workshop and evaluation centers, and facilities that provide financial support or temporary residence arrangements. All of these could be called upon to help the patient in a preventive manner. They could be coordinated, and could work closely in conjunction with the adult deaf community and its various organizations—many of which would be more than glad to help, if given the chance.

One other facility which has enormous preventive potential is the school for the deaf. Schools for the deaf have on their staffs a number of professional personnel whose business it is to see that deaf children develop realistic and mature patterns of adjustment. If these personnel could participate in the planning and development of mental health services and facilities, a solution could surely be found to many problems before the children return to the non-school community. Yet, one of the truest statements I have heard from a workshop went something like this: "Adulthood does not confer employability on a person."

Pupils coming out of a school for the deaf have reached the age of 16, 17, or 18. Physically, they have the appearance of adults. Unfortunately, many of these youngsters crumble under the stress of competitive employment, not to mention competitive training and competitive living. Lest I sound overly critical, let me add that most of them have sufficient resilience to bounce back and recover, to grow and develop. The indications are that schools for the deaf are making a major contribution to the lives of these young adults. It would be even more helpful if, in planning mental health programs for the adult deaf, school personnel could help their students to develop a realistic concept of how different life is going to be in the competitive market and general community from what life and study are in a school for the deaf. The feedback in turn would help the schools towards programs that would reduce the adjustment burden for their graduating teenagers.

SOME MENTAL HEALTH PROBLEMS OF THE DEAF

The adult deaf are a subgroup of our society because they have a severe hearing and/or communication impairment. With less than a half-million deaf adults in the entire population of the country, they are also a minority group. Despite a great deal of effort to help these deaf persons integrate with the general society culturally, equal exposure and development have, for the most part, not yet become a reality for them. Nonetheless, some deaf adults have held their own in social and cultural competition and have moved ahead in the labor market despite their handicap. The adult deaf tend to congregate and socialize among their own kind because of their need to communicate with people in their own way and within their physical limitations, both orally and manually. Among the deaf there are also other sociological groupings, according to educational level, vocational level, avocational interest, religious interest, political interest, cultural interest, or social interest, just as in society as a whole. The smaller the general group, however, the fewer choices one has in which to specialize. The subgroup culture appears to be a difference in degree rather than in kind from the general American culture, with more emphasis upon psychosocial areas where hearing impairment does not hamper the pursuit of one's interests.

Someone once said that deafness shuts one off from people rather than from things. Since most people communicate by means of the spoken word, inability to hear that spoken word not only limits one's communication, but has a great many related psychological features.

It is important for parents, teachers, medical persons, and counselors with hearing to develop a substitute means of helping themselves and the deaf person to communicate especially during his formative years. Language communication is not the only form of communication. Touch, affection, empathy, sympathetic understanding are also important, but a common language reinforces all of these.

The deaf have to be listened to as well as to listen. They have problems that need to be communicated in the best way possible. Their needs are here, present and painful. Their treatment is needed *now*. They cannot first acquire skills that meet the communication demands of society in general before they can unlock themselves from the torment and agony of emotional and mental disturbances. Deafness unquestionably shuts one off from other people and this is precisely where some problems begin.

Mental health problems of the deaf are reflected in attitudes towards one's deafness and towards one's performance and social behavior. They stem from family interrelationships, life for a number of years in an institutionalized setting, and difficulties upon separation from family or from the institutional way of life. There are problems associated with joining an institution or the general community, and with trying to live as an independent, self-supporting citizen. Other difficulties revolve about marriage, sex, unwed motherhood and fatherhood, retirement, acceptance of late-stage deafness, the use of artificial auditory aids, parolees and persons put on probation. Then, too, there are problems of alcoholism, of the socially unaccepted practice of peddling or begging, and a host of possible complications as one is mother, father, son or daughter of a deaf person. There are student problems when dormitory counselors are unable to communicate and problems in obtaining the training necessary to advance in employment. Not all of these areas can be touched upon here.

The vocational rehabilitation counselor should himself have courses of training that deal specifically with actual cases offering psychiatric content and related to mental and emotional illness in general. For my part, I can assure you that my own experience in such a graduate training course was most rewarding, professionally and personally.

DEVELOPING MENTAL HEALTH PROGRAMS

As suggested earlier, the vocational rehabilitation counselor is in a unique position to stimulate and develop mental health services to meet the needs of the deaf. His vocational rehabilitation program will uncover a number of hardcore emotional problems that call for solution before case services can become effective. Existing service gaps can be bridged if the counselor can find the time to build the bridges. Let me outline several areas of need; undoubtedly this conference will add still others.

1. Treatment Programs

a. Children's program: Planning for this would necessarily involve personnel from schools for the deaf, the mental health center, and rehabilitation and community leaders of the deaf. It cannot be assumed that children in schools for the deaf do not have emotional and mental disturbances, so that a program geared specifically to the needs of deaf children could also have a preventive role. Special problems unique to institutional settings need to be dealt with in such a treatment program.

An institutional "family," for example, consists of the child, two, three, or four of his close friends (boys and girls), his dormitory counselor, teacher, guidance counselor, his vocational counselor, and physical education instructor. Institutional sibling rivalry exists, as well as other problems that parallel those found in family living.

Some deaf children have the feeling that living in an institution is equivalent to rejection by their parents. Others, in public schools, may be rejected and ridiculed by hearing fellow students. Deaf children have different problems from the hearing child, and they also have similar problems to a different degree. Preventive mental health should top the list of achievement goals for the program and the counselor.

b. Adolescent treatment program: The vocational rehabilitation counselor must be well aware of the adolescent group and the demands it places on his ingenuity. Experience, together with some psychiatric training, will enable him to distinguish some of the problems already mentioned, and to see where these problems may be created or perpetuated by a given environment. He will note the contribution of the home and the influence of participation in the deaf community or the lack of such participation. He will be able to surmise or to predict the difficulties to be met as the adolescent tries to fit into the competitive labor market, into the hearing community, and into the deaf community of adults. Through planning with other agencies the counselor can often develop an effective rehabilitative and preventive program for deaf adolescents.

c.   Adult treatment program: Here a counselor's prime role would be to guide a mental health center into providing services for the adult deaf through its already established adult treatment program. The counselor must be aware of the manpower shortage, and yet be bold enough to bring about affirmative action.

The most likely problem to be met will be the feelings of helplessness and inadequacy on the part of the center to meet so specialized a need. In my contacts with facilities in the greater Washington area, I have met no other resistance, and we are consequently making plans for a workshop that hopefully will bring into focus the special mental health problems and service needs of the adult deaf.

d.   Geriatric treatment program: Geriatric problems in the entire country can be expected to increase, and deaf adults are not going to be immune. By involving organizations of the deaf and other service groups, a counselor can help plan a mental health program that will enable deaf senior citizens to enjoy a productive life in the years of retirement.

Homes for the aged and schools for the deaf could serve as resources for this type of service. Since there are generally only a few deaf senior citizens in most communities, a tendency exists toward migration to areas where a wider degree of social satisfaction is possible. This must be taken into consideration in planning.

e.   Alcoholic and drug treatment program: Specialized programs in this area may be possible on a statewide basis and perhaps locally in large metropolitan areas. Today considerable attention is already being given to these problems, but the vocational rehabilitation counselor is still the logical person to assist in the development of special services for the alcoholic or addict who is deaf. Leaders of local organizations of the deaf may be able to supply employment opportunities that will help, but the underlying psychological problem calls for professional, medical, and psychotherapeutic assistance.

Peddling or begging might be viewed as another type of addiction. Individuals engaged in this practice, having tasted the relative luxury, wealth, and "fast-living" experiences of this kind of life, find little else attractive. Though they hate their occupation as much as they enjoy it, they are meshed in a vicious cycle from which they see very little chance of escape. Intensive psychotherapy might contribute to the solution of the problem, along with the vocational rehabilitation counselor's efforts to orient them towards more realistically satisfying employment goals.

2. Consultation and Referral Program

The vocational rehabilitation counselor could develop an extensive consultation and referral program at the mental health centers and involve the leaders of the deaf in the planning. If such centers are encouraged to supply mental health information to local organizations of the deaf, the chances will be increased for referrals of deaf adults. In turn, deaf persons will be made more aware of what mental illness and health services are all about, and the preventive potential of such programs will be enhanced.

3. Adult Education

A class in mental health and mental hygiene can assist the adult deaf by giving them wholesome insights into mental health programs. Panels could be set up for open forums and discussion groups, and lectures could be arranged for interested organizations of the deaf.

4. "Out-service" Training Programs

Lay leaders of the deaf community could participate in brief psychotherapeutic experiences, observe psychotherapy in action, and obtain training under mental health service programs in hospitals and mental health settings.

5. Local Workshops

Through case-service funds, a vocational rehabilitation counselor could sponsor local workshops that would involve the discussion (and discovery) of mental health problems that the deaf generally have, and the problems confronting them when they attempt to obtain services from mental health centers. He could probably also recommend solutions so that the needs of the deaf in this area might be more satisfactorily met.

6. Sensitivity Training

A vocational rehabilitation counselor could obtain training to lead Sensitivity Training Groups and try to establish this type of training for deaf adults throughout the community. Various arrangements are possible: The groups could consist, for example, of all deaf persons, of a mixture of deaf and hearing people, or of a mixture of leaders and followers from the deaf community. Such experiences would give deaf individuals a deeper awareness of themselves and the impact that they make on other people, as well as a more meaningful insight into mental illness and into their own feelings of uncertainty with respect to getting along with people who hear.

7. Deaf Community Consultation Program

A vocational rehabilitation counselor can be instrumental in obtaining the deaf consultants that mental health centers will have to rely on for information, as these centers try to develop service programs that will meet the needs of the deaf community.

8. Volunteer Programs

In cooperation with the mental health center or hospital, a counselor can help to organize volunteer groups to become regular visitors of deaf inpatients and outpatients who need assistance in recreation, transportation, or in psychodrama.

9. "Halfway" Adjustment Programs

Since the number of deaf persons who would utilize a halfway house are few and far between, perhaps some arrangement could be made whereby deaf volunteers would offer their own homes to those patients who need "halfway house" assistance until they are able to live independently.

10. Interpreting Program

The vocational rehabilitation counselor could organize a group of interpreters to specialize in an interpreting service program in mental health centers. Such interpreters should receive training with wholesome psychiatric content, including practice interpreting for "mock" psychotherapy sessions. They should also receive training to interpretively assist the clinical psychologist in his testing and therapeutic work. Such interpreting ranges from a high literate use of the sign language to an incoherent and graphic pantomine, according to the communicative skill of the clients to be served. These interpreters should be able to pass a screening examination to become "psychiatric interpreters."

Psychiatric interpreters might even provide supportive counseling and therapy. Interested persons should receive supervised training, and thereupon perform their role under the supervision of a qualified professional.

An interpreter should also have an intimate knowledge of the deaf community. In my experience, a psychotherapist, able to grasp the deaf patient's description of a problem, would often turn to me as interpreter to verify whether interactions in the deaf community were actually as the patient had said. If the interpreter doesn't know the community, he cannot give a meaningful answer. If he does have such intimate knowledge, he is able to identify discrepancies in the patient's report. This can help the therapist bring the patient to a more relevant analysis of his problem.

My experiences do not bear out the idea that an interpreter is an inconvenience in a therapeutic situation. Also, while a one-to-one situation free of communication problems is certainly better for therapy, I do not believe that interpreters are undesirable. Of course there is the possibility that an interpreter can become a discomfort and even a barrier, if he is not qualified to interpret in therapeutic situations. That is why there should be a screening board and an examination that helps to provide for interpreting at various levels. But there are so few psychiatrists and clinical psychologists who are able to work one-to-one with the deaf, that such psychiatric interpreters are a necessity.

11. Health Insurance Aids

Many people, deaf and hearing, are not aware of all the health insurance aids that are available in cases of mental illness. A recent report shows that about half the people in the country are covered by health insurance that provides some mental illness benefits.[2] While reimbursement for hospitalization is more common than for psychiatric office visits, insurance coverage for outpatient visits is on the increase. Of those covered in the survey, 44 percent had policies that provided 50 percent reimbursement for psychiatric bills. About a third could receive as much as 80 percent of the cost, while a fifth had benefits which refunded less than 50 percent of the bill. While no policy covering a group of 500 or more persons completely ruled out benefits for nervous or emotional disorders, smaller groups were found to be more likely restrictive with respect to psychiatric care. Nearly half (48 percent) of the patients in Washington, D. C. receiving inpatient or outpatient psychiatric care reported part of the cost defrayed by health insurance. This compares with 31 percent for Philadelphia and 25 percent for Detroit. New York, Los Angeles, San Francisco and Oakland, St. Louis, Boston, Chicago and Pittsburgh follow, in that order.

The vocational rehabilitation counselor can be instrumental in helping deaf adults to gain as much of such coverage as possible. A knowledge of its availability should reduce apprehension about the high cost of mental health services. An information sheet prepared by an insurance consultant in conjunction with leaders of the deaf community could be helpful if distributed to deaf adults.

12. Lay Counseling by Mental Health Counselors

The subject of lay counseling, close to my heart, is relevant to this workshop and to the therapeutic and counseling needs of the deaf. Since it offers a partial but healthy solution to the mental health services manpower shortage, it is to be hoped that training programs for this work will soon be developed.

Precedents for such programs already exist. With the initial premise that "there never will be enough traditionally trained mental health professionals to meet the treatment and consultation needs of persons suffering from mental and emotional illness and disorder," the National Institute of Mental Health in 1960 began to train lay mental health counselors.[3] The reasoning was that "the profession must recruit talent outside the competitive markets exploited by graduate schools and industry."

Out of a group of 49 applicants, eight housewives were selected. They had had some college experience, their husbands were in a higher-than-average occupational status, and they had had previous paid professional experience. After being given three items of the Wechsler-Bellevue Intelligence test, the Rorschach test, and an abbreviated Thematic Apperception test, they were given four academic semesters of training to prepare them to become Mental Health Counselors.

The experiment showed that these housewives were able to work satisfactorily under supervision as therapists with both adolescents and adults. An indication of community acceptance is the fact that all of these students have been employed in this capacity and expect to continue in their work.

Three additional premises justify a comparable project geared to the needs of the deaf. One is that there may never be enough manpower capable of communication with deaf patients who are in need of therapy. Secondly, even if there were enough interested professionals, they would probably have a difficult time gaining the insights into the deaf community that are needed to provide effective therapy for this specialized group. And thirdly, the manpower turnover would most likely be high in view of the economically unrewarding aspects of this specialized area.

For the deaf, the project could be established in one or several metropolitan communities. Trainees could be highly competent and mature deaf adults or interpreters for the deaf, male or female, and they should undergo a similar screening process to determine whether their basic personal characteristics support their general qualifications to become mental health counselors. Once these persons receive their training, they could, under competent supervision, provide treatment and consultation services for the deaf.

The document describing this work can be obtained for 30 cents.[3] It is urged that the matter be looked into and that the Social and Rehabilitation Service Administration encourage positive action along these lines.

13. Self-Help Groups

Philosophically speaking a person ought to learn first of all to help himself. To quote the late President John F. Kennedy, "God's work must truly be our own," and service organizations exist to help the client to help himself. Don Pettingill has emphasized that excessive services may lead deaf clients to become dependent upon us.[4] In psychiatrist-patient relationships, too, there is a delicate transition as the patient initially becomes dependent upon the psychiatrist to analyze and to solve his problems, and then grows to a point where he arrives at solutions under his own power. With this background it is obvious that programs that do everything for the deaf can only prolong their tradition of dependency. The vocational rehabilitation counselor should help deaf adults to develop attitudes of self-reliance, self-support, initiative, and mature self-help. A committee of leaders of the deaf directed toward developing opportunities of more self-help could be of value, along the lines of already established competitive cultural programs under the Culture Program of the National Association of the Deaf. The self-help program should also be coordinated with the schools for the deaf, so that those aspects of institutional living that contribute to the trait of dependency may be uncovered and eliminated.

With the limited time available, the vocational rehabilitation counselor cannot, of course, do all these things by himself or overnight. The deaf community will probably be the best resource for leadership that he can find, once they receive the needed mental health orientation. Planning with mental health centers alone is not the answer, however, and at the risk of redundancy, let me emphasize that the deaf community must know what it is all about if they are to make proper use of a mental health program.

14. Ministry of the Deaf

Ministers make a real contribution to the spiritual needs of the deaf and should be included in the groups planning programs of mental health services for the deaf. Every counselor should have a registry of clergymen for immediate contact purposes.

SUMMARY AND CONCLUSIONS

I should like this conference to develop a scheme of classification that is applicable to deaf patients in general. The following, taken from a Department of Health, Education, and Welfare publication could provide a starting point for such a classification:

1. Psychosis—the deeper, more far-reaching and prolonged disorders such as schizophrenia and manic-depression

2. Psychoneurosis—a generally less incapacitating functional disorder of the nervous system, in which the personality remains more or less intact

3. Personality, character, and behavior disorders—included in this category are conditions such as pathological or immature personality, alcoholism, drug addiction, etc.[5]

As already noted, the vital components for the truly comprehensive mental health service include: "inpatient services, outpatient services, partial hospitalization, community services, diagnostic services, rehabilitation services, complete care and after-care services, training, research, and evaluation."[6] A Comprehensive Mental Health Service Program for the Deaf should comprise the same types of services but should narrow the focus to the needs of the deaf. Such a program would have special provisions to train professionals and psychiatric interpreters to treat the deaf.

Leaders of the adult deaf community should be encouraged to take an active part in the development of community efforts in behalf of the mentally ill. This is implicit in PL 88-164, the Community Mental Health Centers Act. State vocational rehabilitation agencies and mental health hospitals or rehabilitation centers should make a positive attempt to help counselors of the deaf get the needed training to work in the field of mental health. A part of this effort should include training institutes to give rehabilitation counselors, professional personnel who work with the deaf, and community leaders of the deaf a basic knowledge of the legal and professional framework within which the psychiatrist, the psychologist, and the psychoanalyst work. Psychiatric interpreters should be included in this training. Mobile institutes, traveling from one metropolis to another, should be considered in planning this type of training. Gallaudet College and the National Technical Institute for the Deaf should be encouraged to direct promising young deaf individuals professionally toward the mental health area.

Courses that offer meaningful psychiatric content for such students should be offered, and training programs for rehabilitation counselors of the deaf should include such courses as well as practical experience in psychiatric or mental health centers.

More effort should also be made to define the mental health needs of the deaf and to have this information relayed to schools for the deaf, training programs for rehabilitation counselors, teachers, and other personnel who are training in the area of services to the deaf. Armed with this knowledge, the vocational rehabilitation counselor, the deaf community, and mental health centers could team up to apply for research, training, and demonstration grants for the purpose of developing joint programs for the rehabilitation of mentally ill, recovered, or restored deaf patients.

Perhaps this workshop could outline the requisites of a preventive mental health program which would begin in residential and day schools for the deaf. Supplied with this information, the vocational rehabilitation counselor would be in a better position to make a substantial contribution towards the realization of such a goal.

The vocational rehabilitation counselor has a special responsibility when it comes to supplying the in-hospital and the part-hospitalized patient with rehabilitation services. His work would enable these patients gradually to gain exposure to the community at large and to assume independent living habits within the community. This workshop could define some of the ingredients that go into such a service process.

The needs of other mentally ill deaf persons, not hospitalized but still requiring help to maintain their existence as independent persons in the community, should also receive the attention of this workshop.

The work of the New York State Psychiatric Institute[7] clearly points to a deep need for marriage and family counseling, and counseling on problems related to sexual matters. Young deaf adolescents exposed to misinformation about sex, dating, and marriage, need an opportunity to acquire a mature and meaningful outlook concerning these matters. The vocational rehabilitation counselor would do well to encourage schools for the deaf to develop preventive mental health programs along these lines. Too often, unwed fathers or mothers are expelled outright from schools. The vocational rehabilitation counselor, by developing a cooperative program with the school and social welfare agencies can ease the transfer of these students into the community. It is likely that these persons could benefit from services offered by mental health centers and from special education programs.

As has been shown, there is a wide range of mental health services. A severe shortage of manpower exists generally, and current facilities need to be expanded. Yet services for the deaf are just beginning to emerge. It is possible that, even when this conference is over, we may find we have done nothing more than cleared away the debris or made a few notations on the surface of what is still to be done.

We are fortunate that most major communities do have mental health service programs already established. We painfully accept the fact that they are inadequately staffed and certainly not equipped to deal in depth with the deaf community. We know also that we cannot sit idly by and wait for research and training programs. The people whom we are talking about today, the deaf individuals who need these special services now, are suffering. We must act promptly.

Let us take steps immediately to implement the results of this conference at our local levels. Let us accept this responsibility and meet with psychiatrists, psychologists, administrators, deaf leaders and deaf patients, to apply some of that good, old-fashioned creative hard work to alleviate this suffering.

REFERENCES

1. Albee, G. W.: *Mental Health Manpower Trends*. Basic Books, New York, 1959.

2. Scheidelmandel, P.: *Health Insurance for Mental Illness*. American Psychiatric Association and National Association for Mental Health, Washington, D. C., 1967.

3. Rioch, M. J., Elkes, C. and Flint, A. A.: *Pilot Project in Training Mental Health Counselors*. U. S. Government Printing Office, Washington, D. C., 1965.

4. Pettingill, D.: Vocational rehabilitation programs and problems. *J. Rehab. Deaf, 1*: 47, 1967.

5. *The Rehabilitated Mentally Ill*. Department of Health, Education, and Welfare, U. S. Government Printing Office, Washington, D. C., 1965.

6. Brooks, G. W. and Boag, T. J. (eds.).: *The Psychiatrist's Role in Rehabilitating the Mentally Disabled*. Rehabilitation Services Administration, Washington, D. C., 1964.

7. Rainer, J. D., Altshuler, K. Z., Kallmann, F. J. and Deming, W. E.: *Family and Mental Health Problems in a Deaf Population*. New York State Psychiatric Institute, New York, 1963.

Mental Health: What It Means to the Typical Deaf Person

VICTOR H. GALLOWAY

DESPITE the title of my paper, I would not be so presumptuous as to suggest that I represent the deaf community, or that I am a professional person engaged in mental health services for the deaf. I propose first to present a little of my background. Later I will discuss what I regard as "the typical deaf person."

For several years I was employed as a chemical engineer by a large aerospace company in Northern California. This company employed well over fifty deaf persons in its various processing, manufacturing, and ancillary service areas. Earlier, I had held similar positions in Washington, D. C. and Atlanta. Since graduation from Gallaudet College in 1951, I have been continuously active in organizations of and for the deaf. I am what is often referred to as a "regular, deaf, club man," in that I joined clubs of the deaf in all the cities where I lived, participated in their activities and functions, and held offices in them of one type or another. Being prelingually deaf, I identify easily with the typical deaf person.

As many deaf persons with higher education will tell you, deaf people frequently seek out the better educated among them for aid with their personal problems. This was true in my case, and whenever possible I obliged. Often, however, it was impossible to help because I was not familiar with the various community services that were available to ameliorate the living conditions of those about to succumb to serious mental disorders or emotional disturbances.

So, in 1965, I decided to enter the Leadership Training Program in the Area of the Deaf at San Fernando Valley State College, in order to better prepare myself to help develop community services for the deaf. When I completed the program I was convinced that I should address myself full-time to the problems of deaf people in need of various services. I therefore remained at the State College for a year as a staff member and specialist in adult education.

Since September 1966, I have been a doctoral student in rehabilitation at the University of Arizona and a graduate assistant in its Community Resources Project. The general purpose of this project is to promote better understanding and greater use of rehabilitation concepts within the community. A subproject has been concerned with the deaf population of Tucson. The deaf were chosen to serve as a prototype for establishing communication between a subcommunity and the community at large, thereby increasing the effectiveness of services to that subcommunity.

Let me point out at the outset that the "deaf community" referred to in this paper is made up of *adults* only. Who is the "typical deaf person" who lives in this community and what is he like? Furth[1] has described him as a deaf person who is married to a deaf spouse. He has a stable place of employment, but is unlikely to be holding down a professional or technical position. Generally the job is one in which the ability to communicate is not required. The deaf couple is likely to have children with normal hearing, most deaf children being found in families with hearing parents. Although Furth's description is adequate, I think more background is needed to develop implications about this typical deaf person's mental health, and what the term "mental health" means to him. We should probably know also that he attended a residential school for the deaf for ten to twelve years, and left, holding either an academic diploma or a vocational certificate. He did not make it to Gallaudet College, although he will probably tell you that he could have gone on "if only the school had had good teachers" during his time, or perhaps he might say, "A college degree was not so important then." His reading level is approximately fifth- or sixth-grade level. He is either a printer or a factory assembler earning anywhere from $80 to $120 a week—not too bad, except that he knows that Joe, his hearing friend, on the same assembly line, or holding the same type of job makes ten dollars a week more. In his early twenties, he probably played basketball or bowled for the local club of the deaf, and at times he would serve on committees to raise funds for the team. Between seasons he would just shoot the breeze with his buddies at the deaf club's bar. As he turned thirty, he tried his hand as an officer in some local club of the deaf. Let it be noted here that he had never learned the intricacies of parliamentary procedure nor did he know a ledger from a laundry list! After six years or so of organization work, he probably decided that he had had it, that the splinter factions in his organization had been sniping at him long enough! He declared that he would no longer associate with the deaf and he kept this promise for a while, and dropped out of sight. Two or three years later he began again to show up at the club. He could not quite stay away from his peers. Meanwhile, the club had been having a hard time getting a quorum at its meetings. The club, by the way, is probably located in a not too desirable part of the city, is reached by a flight of dimly lit stairs, and is so poorly lit inside as to create an atmosphere of pervasive gloom. All these factors form a combination not very conducive to a feeling of self-esteem. More on this later.

Many will protest this description of the typical deaf person. Some will refute its negative aspects; others will paint an even more dismal picture. There is no denying, however, that the deaf group forms its own society and its own community, albeit without clearly definable boundaries.

Now what does mental health mean to this typical deaf person? The answer is—nothing! Absolutely nothing!

Our typical deaf person has never encountered the term or at least not the concept of mental health that this conference is meeting to discuss. He may have known of some deaf acquaintance who had been committed to a state hospital, but he could not begin to conceive that mental health services might be applicable to him and to his deaf peers. Mental health? In the sign language these two words are formed by tapping the temple with one forefinger and then tapping in sequence the upper and the lower chest with both hands open. Unfortunately, the signs carry an unfavorable connotation. If he does have some vague awareness of the term, *mental health services,* to the typical deaf person it means mental illness, or, to put it more bluntly, insanity! He does not understand that the competitive demands of civilization often pose a threat to the mental health of even the so-called "normal" individual and that there is a wide range of services that could help him cope with his own difficulties or problems. Because mental health services still suggest to him a complete psychological breakdown, he may refuse to avail himself of what services are available in the community. Douglas Burke noted in a recent article that client resistance and negative feelings toward treatment pose one of the great problems in developing mental health services for the deaf.[2]

The entire field of mental health is so surrounded with mysticism that it is seemingly impenetrable to the typical deaf person. He himself will have no use for counseling or therapy, and he is apt to adopt a punitive attitude towards those who have availed themselves of such services. Until such time as the deaf community can be brought to recognize mental illness or emotional disturbance as a social problem which touches every member of society, the rehabilitation of deaf patients will continue to be extremely difficult—even if the needed resources and personnel were available. Let me illustrate with a case.

A social welfare agency called concerning Mrs. A., a deaf woman in her fifties, who seemed in need of psychiatric and social help. Her husband had died an untimely death, and she was ill-prepared to cope with the management of his estate. It had seemed fortunate that Mrs. A. had been referred to the only agency (of forty in the community) that had a person trained in social work and experienced in working with the deaf. But, while the social worker could fingerspell somewhat and use sign language after a fashion, he simply could not communicate well enough to establish a helping relationship with the client. Mrs. A. was unhappy, and it was believed that she needed fellowship with other deaf persons and protection from herself. The agency requested help in finding a congenial home atmosphere, hopefully with a family who would take her in to live with them and would understand her problem. There was concern that if nothing was forthcoming, an institution would be Mrs. A.'s next stop.

Since it was acknowledged that institutionalization would be a grave mistake and certainly would not help Mrs. A., the request from the agency could not be refused. As was expected, the deaf shied away from the idea of taking in a person who was receiving mental health services. "Mental, did you say? Not on your life!" was the typical reaction. The agency was informed that efforts to locate a place for Mrs. A. had been unsuccessful and no more was heard from them for several weeks. Then an urgent call came from the Suicide Prevention Clinic, appealing for a deaf person to come to the Center immediately and see if he could somehow establish meaningful communication with a deaf client. The client turned out to be the same Mrs. A. for whom a home had been sought in vain.

The deaf volunteer went to the Center and sat in on a session with Mrs. A. and the psychologist. The deaf client kept talking about how suicide would end it all and relieve everyone of the problem she believed she was causing. She had been using the oral method of communication exclusively with the psychologist. She was an excellent lip-reader, although it was obvious to the volunteer that she was under a great deal of strain. At the same time the psychologist was not fully able to understand everything Mrs. A. said and as a result was unable to react to all of her feelings. He was forced to operate at the cognitive level and this quite naturally was frustrating for the client.

It finally became necessary for the deaf volunteer to participate in the relationship. He used the combined method of communication, that is, he used the language of signs and at the same time mouthed the words. This greatly reduced the communication barrier and permitted Mrs. A. to deal more directly with her problem.

Would that I could report a happy ending, but unfortunately this was not the case. When Mrs. A. had regained her composure and felt confident enough to venture out into the deaf society, she ran into immediate, covert rejection. She was quick to sense this, and indeed it was evident to the deaf volunteer who by coincidence was at a social function Mrs. A. attended. She soon regressed to her former condition and worse.

There is no question that the need is great for more adequately trained professional personnel, including psychiatrists, clinical psychologists, psychometrists, vocational counselors, dormitory counselors, and many others, and that steps should be taken immediately to close the gap in services provided by such professionals. But along with the recruitment of well-trained personnel, there should also be preparation of the deaf community for receiving rehabilitated persons back into their midst. In recent years great strides have been made to educate the general public about the nature of mental illness and the possibility of its prevention and cure. Only very recently have pychologists and psychiatrists begun to focus on the mental health needs of the deaf, and it is quite understandable that the deaf community have not yet been made aware of this new hope.

In the education of the general public concerning the attainment and maintenance of mental health the trend is to emphasize the similarity between neurotic illness and physical illness. It is my fear that with the deaf this will not work. The typical deaf person deals with the concrete and not the abstract. He must be led to realize that while physical illness results from disease or trauma of some type, neurotic illness is an outgrowth of conflict between person and person, or person and self. Furthermore, he must be brought to understand that, unlike physical illness which can be cured by drugs or other forms of medication, neurotic illness must frequently be helped by interactions between the patient and other important individuals.

An interesting similarity between the manifestations of emotional disorder and of deafness is that neither fits the medical model. There are no apparent lesions, changes in the size of organs, fluctuations in temperature, or other physical anomalies. When John Doe seems nervous, "talks funny," or acts "crazy," he is said to have a mental health problem. Many a well-adjusted deaf person has been perceived in like manner. What is perceived is concerned with his social behavior, the ways in which he interacts with others. This blurring of boundaries could be the reason why in earlier days schools for the deaf were often called "asylums."

It is vitally important, then, that deaf people be involved in mental health programs and the approach should be as to "a social problem (rather) than a technologic one, a problem of society rather than simply of professionals, a problem of the community."[3]

Thus far we have only attempted a description of the typical deaf person and tentatively answered the question posed by the title of this paper. At this time it should be appropriate to attempt a definition of *mental health*. According to Louis Thorpe, "Definitions are either nonexistent in any practical sense or are so inclusive that they involve every facet of the life of man, including man himself."[4] He views mental health from two different points of view: (1) the absence of symptoms of maladjustment, such symptoms ranging along a continuum from feelings of inferiority or guilt, through psychosomatic disorders and the psychoneuroses, to the organic and functional psychoses; (2) the satisfactory adaptation to requirements of group life, whereby the individual experiences the greatest success permitted by his abilities, with a maximum sense of well-being on his own part and the highest possible benefit to society.

It is, of course, extremely difficult to reduce such terms to an understandable level for our typical deaf person. As long as he is "working hard" or "feels OK" he can point to these criteria and tell himself and others that there is no need to probe further into his condition. One other difficulty is the matter of cultural bias. Without specific reference to the deaf community, I should like to mention Thorpe's further observation that a "sick society" may accept, as normal or desirable, behavior which is obviously emblematic of a disturbed personality, i.e., an ethnic group may have its own idea as to the meaning of mental health. As an instance, Hollywood personalities use psychiatric services nearly as often as they take aspirin. But another group may view mental health in an entirely different light, and possibly the deaf group's ideas and understanding of mental health are different from those of the general public.

Another question arises: What are the requirements for every individual if he is to be mentally healthy? Patterson[5] suggests that he must have at least a modicum of self-esteem, that he must accept himself, that he must feel that at least in some respects he is a person of worth. He even postulates that every person is basically driven and motivated to achieve and to maintain this sense of self-esteem. But how does one develop self-esteem? Obviously, the social environment must be one that facilitates its development. This often comes to my mind when my thoughts turn to the gloomy club room for the deaf, up the dimly lit stairs in the Bottom Heights section of a city.

A new way to mental health for the deaf is being paved by the excellent group in New York, and other fine programs are developing in St. Louis, Wichita, and Pittsburgh, to name just a few. The New York group has frequently involved the deaf community in the planning and development of programs for the mentally ill or emotionally disturbed deaf. This is a model that the rest of the nation may well emulate.

With regard to new ways toward mental health, I am reminded of an address delivered by the late Dr. Martin Luther King. Addressing the convention of the Southern Christian Leadership Conference in Atlanta in 1967, he said, "There is probably no way, even eliminating violence, for Negroes to obtain their rights without upsetting the equanimity of white folks. Negroes will be *mentally healthier* (emphasis mine) if they do not suppress rage but vent it constructively and . . . peacefully . . . to cripple the operations of an oppressive city." Scattered all over the city were large posters proclaiming "Black is beautiful." When asked the meaning of it all, a Negro replied, "This is our new way to mental health." It would, of course, be facetious to suggest that the deaf should put up posters proclaiming "Deaf is perfect." But like the Negroes, the deaf need to develop more self-esteem and a better self-image. It is conceivable that there may be other ways to mental health for the deaf not yet explored.

The Social and Rehabilitation Service has frequently called for more basic research in the deaf community and the subculture that it represents. Much has also been said in support of moving the deaf into the community at large. The argument is that the present semi-isolation from the general public leads to a social environment that oppresses, and hence to a deterioration in the well-being of the deaf. Beatrice

Wright[6] suggested certain measures to enhance the attitudes of the community at large toward disability. She argued for the integration of children with disabilities into the regular schools whenever feasible, so that familiarity with physical deviation takes place in natural settings. She proposed that "it is less the physical deviation as such that creates a feeling of being different than the psychological characteristics imputed to the person through the phenomenon of spread."[6] She also reviewed factors that are important to resolving discrepancies in expectation. Commonly the hearing person holds higher expectations with respect to a person who is deaf, than are borne out, because the deaf person, looking just like anyone else, is expected to act like anyone else. For example, the hearing person expects the deaf person to be able to communicate with him, but finds that he cannot. Reconciliation of the discrepancy is effected, but often with some damage to the deaf person's self-esteem.

In one way or another, it is always the problem of communication that interferes, that makes it difficult to work with the mentally ill deaf patient, and that prevents the deaf from seeking or understanding mental health services. Wright oversimplifies the requirements for prevention of mental disorders in the deaf when she suggests that the community at large should become familiar with and accept physical deviation. While this is, of course, desirable, the deaf themselves must also be apprised of the ramifications of their disability, including its implications for their mental health. It might be advisable for schools for the deaf to take their students aside and explain what deafness is all about, frankly discussing the limitations imposed by this disability. This could then be followed by discussions as to how these limitations can be circumvented and how inherent strengths can be capitalized upon. As a layman, I, too, may be oversimplifying things, but it seems a worthwhile suggestion.

I should like to ask the forbearance of the professionals in the field if I digress a bit in an effort to further discuss the communication problem as it bears on the mental health of the deaf. Rogers has noted that:

> much of the counseling of adults is done on a private basis by psychiatrists and psychologists. There has been, however, in recent years, a development of advisory and counseling services in the field of marital adjustment. . . . In such services, although physical examinations, legal advice, and other elements may enter to some extent into the service, the basic tool of the worker is the counseling process.[7]

Obviously, the client's participation in the process is essential.

Attention was directed to the methodology of counseling[8] when the mental health movement first started in 1908 with the publication of Clifford Beers' book, *The Mind That Found Itself*. Also about that time the distinction was made between counseling and psychotherapy, a difference perhaps useful to point out here. Psychotherapy attempts to enable a person to get rid of his difficulties by talking about them—

with the aim of a personality change of some sort. Counseling generally refers to a helping process which does not purport to change the person, but rather to enable him to utilize the resources he has for coping with life. In either case, however, interaction is the fulcrum upon which process operates. Remember, our typical deaf person reads at the fifth- or sixth-grade level and uses the language of signs. Where does he go to obtain this type of counseling service? To any worker in any mental health agency? Of course not. There are far too few mental health specialists who are able to communicate with the deaf via the language of signs, and when the deaf need help, they usually turn to other sources for aid. They generally seek out those with whom they can feel comfortable and, hence, "a great many ministers, deaf and hearing, are by circumstances forced to act in a field where normally the social worker is found. . . ."[9]

These ministers usually make it a point to learn the language of signs and to circulate in the deaf community to further increase their manual skill. They no longer limit their services to those of purely religious nature but also include mental health services. "Mental health is a common pulpit topic; and to the twin concepts of 'sin and salvation' has been added, a third 'and society.' "[10] These persons are sought out for help not because they are ministers but rather because they can use the language of signs. Whether or not they can really help the troubled ones is almost beside the point.

A disquieting thought about the use of sign language in a therapeutic relationship is implied by a statement of Baroff's. He said:

> . . . in the mental health specialty where verbal communication is a therapeutic as well as diagnostic agent, the deaf person seeking psychiatric assistance is at a disadvantage. . . . Manual language is ill-suited for communication of abstract ideas—that which is primarily symbolic. Yet it is through the use of abstraction that much of our information is formulated and disseminated.[11]

But, the inescapable fact remains that the language of signs is the medium through which the deaf client must often be reached. Methods must be developed to utilize this language effectively.

In the deaf community, word gets around rapidly. Once a person in need of help with some of his problems obtains satisfaction, an avalanche of similar requests is likely to follow. In 1966, a new project designed to expand and extend educational opportunities to the adult deaf was initiated at San Fernando Valley State College, and a deaf graduate of its Leadership Training Program was brought in to head the project. During the early weeks the specialist was called upon to help a few deaf people with problems that were not at all connected with the project itself. It was not long before the project office was swamped with calls for help. The situation reached such proportions that the specialist was compelled to visit clubs of the deaf to explain the real nature of his project, and to suggest other places where help could be obtained. It was interesting to note that with several agencies in the general area serving the deaf, the deaf themselves preferred to take their problems to the project leader who was deaf, even though he obviously was not equipped to handle them. A survey of mental health resources in Metropolitan Dallas found that "services of a counseling and therapeutic nature, i.e., psychological evaluation, psychiatric evaluation, marital counseling, child and family counseling, and ministerial counseling are not being used to the extent that one might assume desirable."[12] If these agencies were staffed with workers skilled in the language of signs, this situation would change overnight. The ability to communicate with professionals easily and comfortably means much to the mental health of the typical deaf person.

In Tucson we have recently had a classic example of how important it is for professionals in community service agencies to work in cooperation with persons skilled in the language of signs when attempting to help deaf clients. A deaf Mexican, the father of eight children, applied for his naturalization papers approximately a year ago. Part of the procedure called for his obtaining verification of his residence in two other states. Initially, he attempted to get the required verifications by visiting these two states and asking two friends in each state to execute the forms to be mailed to the Office of Immigration and Naturalization. He finally received notice from the Office that they were recommending that his petition for naturalization be denied because the required forms had not been filed. He had been in a mental turmoil all along and this increased his anguish and anxiety. Finally, he contacted a deaf person familiar with community agencies, who enlisted the assistance of a hearing friend and an agency worker. Just a week ago word was at last received that all the requirements for his naturalization had been met. If the Mexican had gone to the agency first, he would have met with frustration after frustration, for he had only a smattering of English and the signs that he used were very elementary and crude. Likewise, if the deaf person who helped him and his hearing friend had not made the contacts with the appropriate agency, the problem probably would still be unresolved. The man might have reached a breaking point if he had not been able to obtain the necessary help. This case illustrates the need for teamwork in providing mental health services to the deaf. It also is an example of preventive care.

With regard to the deaf community, what are some of the ways in which its citizens can ensure that mental health services would be available to them? Almost always, there are a few deaf persons who are above average in intelligence and understanding of the demands imposed on them by society (and the burden *should* be theirs to act as catalysts), who initiate community action and team up with professionals in the field to develop the needed services. In those situations where the deaf lack the necessary sophistication in community development, the professionals may have to initiate action. At a conference of social workers held several years ago the professionals,

. . . in apparent recognition of the deaf's reticence, agreed that they should take the responsibility of identifying needs in potential problem areas and make social services available and of stimulating an awareness of the social and emotional needs of the deaf persons and his family in order to enrich such services.[13] Dr. Rainer[14] has suggested that for most deaf persons, the most important recommendations in the field of mental health planning lie in the preventive area. . . . The most fruitful approach to prevention of maladjustment is to center attention on preparation for family living, since it is in this context that most unhappiness and behavior disorders manifest themselves.

It is encouraging to note that a few highly specialized services are developing. Mental health services, in particular, are still in their early stages but the prospects for further growth and expansion are excellent. It is yet too early to measure the full effect of these programs, but initial accomplishments are very encouraging.[15]

At the National Conference on Education of the Deaf, held in Colorado Springs in 1967, a number of recommendations were made, ranging from regional mental health programs for the deaf that would incorporate service, training, and research, to establishing centers within the framework of existing facilities to emphasize leadership training. It was noted that leadership opportunities should be provided for the deaf themselves, and provision should be made for advanced study by qualified deaf adults and for their participation in the planning and implementation of programs for the deaf at all levels. With implementation of each of these recommendations, the day will come when the deaf will recognize mental illness and emotional disturbance as a social problem, and they will take active roles in developing a social environment that, by fostering mental health, will permit them to take their rightful places in society.

REFERENCES

1. Furth, H. G.: *Thinking Without Language*. The Free Press, New York, 1966.
2. Burke, D. J.: D. C. vocational rehabilitation for the deaf: A high rise model. *J. Rehab. Deaf, 1:* 3, 1967.
3. Ryan, W.: Citizens in mental health—what are they for. *Mental Health, 50:* 597, 1966.
4. Thorpe, L. P.: *The Psychology of Mental Health*. Ronald Press, New York, 1960.
5. Patterson, C. H.: Counseling as a relationship. In *Readings in Rehabilitation* (C. H. Patterson, ed.). Stipes Publishing, Champaign, Ill., 1960.
6. Wright, B. A.: *Physical Disability—A Psychological Approach*. Harper & Row, New York, 1960.
7. Rogers, C.: *Counseling and Psychotherapy*. Houghton Mifflin, Cambridge, Massachusetts, 1942.
8. Tyler, L. E.: *The Work of the Counselor*. Appleton-Century-Crofts, New York, 1961.

9. Best, H.: *Deafness and the Deaf in the United States.* Macmillan, New York, 1943.

10. Mowrer, O. H.: Some philosophical problems in psychological counseling. *J. Couns. Psychol.,* 4: 2, 1957.

11. Baroff, G. S.: Patterns of socialization and community integration. In *Family and Mental Health Problems in a Deaf Population.* (Rainer, J. D., Altshuler, K. Z. and Kallmann, F. J., eds.). New York State Psychiatric Institute, New York, 1963.

12. Resources in the Metropolitan Dallas area for patients with communication disorders. A Project Report submitted by The Callier Hearing and Speech Center, Dallas, Texas, 1967.

13. Galloway, V. H.: Problems related to social agencies and the deaf adult. Unpublished paper. San Fernando Valley State College, Northridge, California, 1965.

14. Rainer, J. D. and Kallmann, F. J.: Preventive mental health planning. In *Family and Mental Health Problems in a Deaf Population* (Rainer, J. D., Altshuler, K. Z. and Kallmann, F. J., eds.). New York State Psychiatric Institute, New York, 1963.

15. Craig, W. N.: Rehabilitation of the deaf: Threshold of innovation. A Presentation at the Middle States Institute on the Vocational Rehabilitation of the Deaf. Pittsburgh, Pennsylvania, 1967.

The Contributions of Social Work Practice to the Mental Health of the Hearing Impaired

SIDNEY N. HURWITZ

THE PRESENT title perhaps reflects the fantasies of the author more than it does the content of the article itself. For, as the following material will confirm, it is somewhat fanciful to speak of a social work "contribution" to the mental health of hearing-impaired persons; up to now any contribution by social work to this field of service has been miniscule. I am not aware of a single book related to hearing impairment written by a social worker; professional articles on this subject, written by social workers, have been extremely few and generally quite superficial in nature. The actual numbers of social workers believed to be practicing in organizations primarily devoted to services for the deaf and hard of hearing are extremely small. The "contribution," then, implied in the title of this paper is not one of past or current accomplishment; it is rather one of promise and anticipation only, a reference to future potentialities and expectations.

This paper presents first a statistical report of the present amount and nature of social worker participation in the field; second, a brief theoretical review of characteristics of social work practice. Third, I plan to relate theory to practice, focusing first on certain observed personality deficiencies of deaf youth, and then examining future possibilities for enhancing social work contributions to this particular population.

Survey of Social Worker Utilization

After accepting the present assignment I was not a little chagrined to realize that, beyond my personal experiences, I had virtually no firsthand acquaintance with social work activity among the deaf and hard of hearing. About three years ago I had advertised for a social worker to fill a staff position in a program for the deaf and, after four

63

futile months, was ready to concede, like many an aging spinster, that what I sought either didn't exist or was immune to my seductions. That social workers serving the deaf do exist, though in modest numbers, was demonstrated through a survey I conducted in October 1967. This survey undertook to learn the extent of social worker utilization by the three major groups of professional organizations serving the hearing impaired: educational facilities, rehabilitation and related service programs, and speech and hearing clinics. Information regarding the staffing of speech and hearing clinics is available in the *American Annals of the Deaf,* and the statistics quoted for this group of facilities derive from the May 1967 issue of the *Annals.*

The remainder of the data was collected by means of a questionnaire distributed to 107 schools and 26 service organizations listed in the *Annals* as "Rehabilitation Centers and Facilities." All state-supported residential schools, private residential and day schools, and public day schools were surveyed. No attempt was made to survey day classes. The questionnaire asked each organization to indicate whether they employed social workers whose major responsibilities were to deaf persons and, if not, whether they would employ such personnel if they were available. Social work employers were asked to note how many they employed, whether full or part time, and extent of professional training; and to select from a list of eight service activities those being performed by social work staff. A final question, addressed to employers and non-employers, asked for a judgment as to what a social worker's "contribution *can be*" in a comprehensive approach to assisting deaf children and adults in their social and emotional development."

Out of the sample of 133 separate facilities, 86 responded: 43 state-supported schools, 25 private residential schools and private and public day schools, and 18 service organizations. Only 25 (or 29 percent) of the 86 facilities responding employed at least one social worker. A total of 28 social workers worked in these 25 facilities. Out of a total of 203 speech and hearing clinics listing staff complements in the *Annals,* less than 10 percent included a social worker in the clinical team. The first and most obvious conclusion to be drawn from these data is that professional workers predominantly associated with serving the hearing impaired—primarily educators and audiologists—do not view the role of social work practitioners as a basic or unique one in mental health services for this population.

Survey information provides material also for some conclusions about the tasks social workers perform in two of the three major settings surveyed. Looking first at social work (15 schools reported having a social worker on the staff), the social work role most frequently mentioned was one in relation to parents and families of the students: family investigation, guiding the family in planning for their child, establishing satisfying relationships between family and child, serving as liaison between home and school. It is worthy of note that a great many school administrators who do *not* employ social workers, but who specified they would like to add them to their staff, emphasized that the major service that could be provided was in relation to the families of students. Here is a typical comment as expressed by one school administrator: "(The social worker can provide) liaison between school and home. I feel we have a tremendous gap between parents and school which is a disadvantage to the pupil, parent, and school."

Other social work functions referred to with about equal frequency were: 1) handling admissions procedures, intake studies, obtaining social histories, and the like; 2) counseling students; 3) assisting students in the acquisition of social skills, helping them apply these skills in the community, and helping students make greater utilization of community resources; 4) serving as liaison between teachers and students, community and school, community services and students. State-supported residential schools which reported the smallest percentage of social work staff (14 percent) tended almost entirely to view social work expertise as limited in application to certain specific areas as noted above. Private residential and public and private day schools (with a 36 percent rate of social worker utilization) tended to view the use of this discipline in considerably broader terms—in effect, as an integral member of the faculty team who participates in various levels of planning and decision making. For example, while all alluded to the five aforementioned areas of social work activity, a number submitted the concept that "(social workers) counsel with teachers to try to find acceptable ways to help the deaf child in the learning situation." This function, it might be added parenthetically, has generally been considered a major function of the public school social worker, that is, to assist the teacher in doing a better job with the child. Others referred to the concept of social workers being part of "a comprehensive team approach to help parents and families accept the handicap of deafness and to help the child obtain the most he can from his educational opportunity." One school elaborated on the social worker-as-team-member concept in this way: "to participate in assessment of student strengths and in programming for release of their capacities to the fullest and for the maximum prevention and/or reduction of handicapping effects of impairments." Another informant stressed the value of the social worker's sharing with the faculty team information on community resources.

It seems significant that both private and public residential schools rarely utilize social workers for houseparents training or supervision. One social worker in a public residential school wrote that this function was a major responsibility of hers, but apparently her case was exceptional.

Service programs hiring social workers would appear to utilize them in rather traditional ways: for psychosocial evaluation of home and family, for consultation to other staff in diagnosis, evaluation, and various types of planning for clients, in direct counseling to clients and families, in liaison between client and community resources. Even though almost half the reporting facilities do not have a staff social worker, responses both from employers and non-employers suggest that social work in service facilities tends to be integrated on a par with other disciplines and to be considered a vital supportive service.

To summarize, the quantitatively small amount of social work utilization in this field is expended scarcely at all on state residential school populations which train about one-half of deaf youngsters, rather marginally on other schools, and proportionately in greatest degree in facilities serving adults. These conclusions epitomize the great concern the writer has for mental health services to the deaf. Social work utilization, in and of itself, is not an adequate yardstick for measuring the adequacy of mental health programming except insofar as underutilization of social work expertise, it would seem, almost always goes hand-in-hand with underutilization of other essential mental health resources. There is little doubt that another survey to determine utilization of psychiatrists, psychologists, and teacher counselors would necessitate the conclusion that these disciplines also are grossly underutilized. My greatest concern, however, is that long-established mental health principles and practices relating to the healthy development of children and youth are being denied large segments of our deaf children. Social work underutilization, particularly for children, is merely one indicator of this condition.

Psychosocial Problems of Deaf Youth

At this point a brief personal note may be in order. Prior to my introduction to rehabilitation for the deaf, I was engaged a number of years in the field of child welfare. Some of these years involved working with children who had been placed in institutions for treatment of their emotional disorders. It is striking that many of the same characteristics I formerly saw among emotionally disturbed children I now see embodied in the 17-, 18-, 19- and 25-year-old deaf people who are enrolled in the program with which I am affiliated. It is well known to the conference participants that many deaf young people emerge into adulthood grossly lacking in the prerequisite personality characteristics necessary for mature relationships and responsible adult behavior.

Here are some of these individuals:

Pat is 28 years old. Since terminating her training in a residential school at age 19 she has lived in five different communities where she worked at low-skill jobs. She is extremely inhibited sexually, always fearful that she will not be able to control her impulses, alternately depreciating sex and exaggerating its role in relationship between the sexes. She tends to be chronically depressed, socially passive, and isolated. She deals with her problems by perpetually fantasizing some future situation that will bring her greater personal satisfaction than she now enjoys. These fantasies provide her rationalization for not taking constructive action in the present. She is almost totally preoccupied with thoughts of herself and shows little sensitivity to others. Her chronic pattern of moving about is a result of her dissatisfaction with her present reality and her means of avoiding greater investment in the present.

Louise is 19 and recently terminated from a deaf day school. Her characteristic expression is bland and detached. She is intensely constricted. When a lengthy period of counseling was able to break through some of her constriction, she attempted to use the counselor only as a waste basket for her complaints, avoiding personal responsibility for her behavior. Faced with expectations of responsible behavior she would withdraw into hostile constriction. She was incapable of making friendships. In her loneliness she indiscriminately accepted overtures from boys, though obviously fearful of sexual involvement. She practices what we term "emotional blackmail": "Either play the game by my rules or I will withdraw from you."

Paul is 19 and a residential school student since he was 6. He is a con man, extremely ingratiating toward adults, quite clever in presenting his wishes and gaining the attention and services he requires. He displays relatively little interest in achieving anything on his own, most of his energies being directed toward manipulating others to do things for him. He accepts little responsibility for his own behavior; he lies a great deal and/or projects blame to avoid criticism. His superficially happy facade very thinly masks a great deal of hostility which he fears expressing and which, instead, emerges through crying.

Martin, 21 years old, was discharged from day school at 16 because of persistent homosexual overtures, some forcibly perpetrated on young boys. He is intensely bitter towards others, deeply pessimistic about himself and his future. At times he becomes enraged and is unable to control himself. His experience in a facility workshop revealed that he can be quite productive in a sheltered environment that is highly accepting of him and constantly rewarding to him. Subsequent history on jobs indicates that he will not be productive when employers treat him as an adult.

Joan is 26; her lifelong pattern has been one of underachievement, dependency, and withdrawal from stressful situations. She is compulsively preoccupied with all facets of her physical person and with her perceptions of loneliness and rejection. This compulsive rumination and oversensitivity to her own needs interfere with productivity; she gives little concentrated attention to tasks. Though characteristically bland and detached, she shows flashes of anger when pushed for more responsible behavior. Though she verbalizes a great deal about her wishes for recognition, she avoids both relationships and productivity that might bring recognition.

What do the five people depicted in these vignettes have in common? All are profoundly deaf. All are representative of most deaf young adults insofar as they have intelligence within the normal range, have had prolonged specialized education, are physically healthy, and for the most part have achieved academically on a par with their schoolmates, albeit on quite a deficient level. The major impairment they suffer in common is one of retarded personality development; this impairment, rather than deafness *per se* or low academic functioning *per se* or other handicaps, blocks their continued growth and progress. During the past two and one-half years our program has studied 165 deaf individuals, most of whom have been designated by Vocational Rehabilitation counselors in several states as persons least capable of benefiting from existing rehabilitation facilities in their own localities. A major conclusion of our studies is that these clients, regardless of what combination of other handicaps they possess, are most impaired by their problems of psychosocial functioning. They are armed poorly, with infantile and childish techniques for adapting to an adult world.

Two broad categorizations* become apparent. The first profile is one we termed the "Underdeveloped Personality." Individuals in this group are characterized by infantile and inadequate behavior patterns. They tend to be highly dependent people, lacking in initiative, fearful of new events. Their limitations bind their energies to the immediate present. They do not make effective use of whatever mechanics and knowledge they possess for communication and are equally inept in socialization and self-sufficient functioning. Serious deficits in work orientation exist. Such individuals, within the very limited purview of their experience and personality structure, tend to view reality correctly but lack adequate adaptive responses. Maturational underdevelopment is displayed in their lack of heterosexual development, in their infantile defense mechanisms, in the poverty of their response repertoire to emotionality.

A second fundamental categorization is one we termed the "Maldeveloped Personality." Herein we include the pathological or the disturbed individual. This individual is characterized by inappropriate responses, preoccupation with internal stimuli, and dominance of his primary needs and drives. He may be fixated or regressed. Many seek interaction with others but the nature of the interactions they promote is destructive, manipulative, need-determined, or otherwise ineffective in furthering their development. Ego integrity is brittle; their functional adjustment is marginal. By contrast with the "Underdeveloped Personality" who characteristically displays passive defenses, persons in this second group tend to act out under stress. In this broad group we find a number of highly pathological individuals who exhibit psychotic-like behavior.

Much of the work that will involve us in future years will be in the prevention of psychosocial retardation among our deaf young people. This will be a formidable task, in light of what is suspected of the cognitive, perceptual, neurosensory communication, as well as the psychological complexities of deafness. I refer only, or primarily, to the psychosocial aspects of the problem. In this connection a valuable guide is already available. To quote from the well-known New York State Psy-

---

* For this behavioral construct we are grateful to Sal DiFrancesca, clinical psychologist, and Nicholas Colarelli, clinical consultant to the Rehabilitation Program for the Deaf and Hard of Hearing, St. Louis Jewish Employment and Vocational Service.

chiatric Institute report on "Family and Mental Health Problems in a Deaf Population":

> For most deaf persons, the important recommendations in the field of mental health planning lie in the preventive area. Conditions leading to frustration, poor adjustment, and sexual and other forms of delinquency arise within the matrix of the family and the early residential setting of the school. Deaf adolescents grow up and go on to parenthood, often without adequate knowledge and guidance. The most fruitful approach to prevention of maladjustment is to center attention on preparation for family living since it is in this context that most unhappiness and behavior disorders manifest themselves. Certainly education and vocational training are also important, but to be effective they require an emotionally stable student. . . .[1]

Characteristics of Social Work

The key phrase in the above statement bears repetition: "The most fruitful approach to prevention of maladjustment is to center attention on preparation for family living." I believe it is precisely in the area of preparation for family living that social work can make its most significant contribution toward alleviation of the problems of deafness. Before plunging into some ideas about the nature of this contribution, a brief review of the nature of social work itself is indicated. This is necessary because the ubiquitous, extremely diverse, and often ambiguous character of social work practices tend to confuse both the general public and colleagues with whom social workers share service responsibilities. To date, the failure of social work to define a systematic body of knowledge and values doubtless also contributes to the problem of the profession in clearly articulating and interpreting its purposes and methods. What is often perceived as social work practice tends to be no more than a few, isolated, highly visible aspects of practice: social studies of clients, foster home placements of children, the giving of tangible assistance, and the like.

Social work is one of the helping professions. Its avowed aim is to "assist individuals and groups to identify and resolve or minimize problems arising out of disequilibrium between themselves and their environment."[2] The technical aspects of this concept will be enlarged upon later; it may suffice to note here that social work is largely concerned with the balance between man and his environment, looking not at man alone but at man-in-his-situation and in-his-relations to other people. The critical dimensions of social work are the individual and society.

The most laudable characteristic of social work, and the source of its most splendid record, when it has been willing to exercise this function, has consisted of a willingness to act as the conscience of the community in behalf of hosts of outcast peoples whose status or behaviors relegated them beyond the pale of society. At its best, social work has consisted of acts of enlightened compassion. The field of social work is, today, at the forefront of legislation and programs for correcting the ravages of poverty, family breakdown, the displacement of the aged in our society, and so on. In this regard, social work exercises both its ethical and value beliefs and its technical expertise in the organization and implementation of programs of social rehabilitation and amelioration. This same system of values and purpose is translated to the realm of the individual where, as Bartlett points out, there is the "perspective by which social workers stand consistently beside the individual being helped, viewing the situation from their viewpoint and seeking to understand its meaning to them."[3]

Social work is, however, more than a function of its philosophy and value structure. With other professions it shares a knowledge base. This base is eclectic, drawn from psychoanalytic psychiatry, dynamic and social psychology, sociology, cultural anthropology, and other disciplines. This knowledge is directed toward the end of bringing about improved interaction between individuals or groups of individuals and the environment. Out of concern for internal man and his external world social work strives towards knowledge of both as discrete entities. Social workers, in their two years of graduate training, study the community, its internal processes, modes of development and change, its social services and resources. They also study human development and behavior, the meaning and effects on people, of cultural heritage, of religious beliefs, of law and other social institutions, the ways in which people communicate with one another and give outer expression to inner feelings, group processes, and the effects of groups upon individuals.

Complementing knowledge of either man or society is knowledge of the interactional processes between the two: what the reciprocal influences of man and his total environment are, the reciprocal influences of the individual and his social group (as, e.g., the family group), what the nature of relationships is between individuals. And there is a final kind of knowledge indispensible to the social work practitioner: knowledge of himself, his emotions and attitudes as they affect his professional functions.[2]

A profession must also have at its disposal an arsenal of methods and techniques to implement its purposes. Depending on the setting in which social workers operate and the nature of their responsibilities, they have traditionally engaged in three rather loosely defined areas of practice: social casework, social group work, and community organization. Methodologies have varied considerably among these three areas. Social casework has tended to employ those techniques of interpersonal influence which have been drawn from psychoanalytic psychiatry, though focusing primarily on conscious aspects of the ego toward the end of activating and supporting existing personality strengths. Aspects of education and environmental manipulation have also played a part in these techniques. Social group work has aimed largely at the level of affecting individuals through their involvement in the group and at the level of enhancing group behaviors. A major tool for the group worker has been the manipulation of group activities, organization, purposes, and structure. The community organization worker, in addition to techniques for information getting, has relied heavily on systems for collective problem solving, program evaluation, and program implementation.

What is germane to the present discussion is that all of these methods have applicability to all populations including, of course, the deaf. A second consideration is that, as in every profession, full academic training in an accredited graduate school is indispensable for optimum growth and performance on the part of practitioners. Social work is indeed an art, but it is art that cannot be effectively applied, developed, and perfected without a conceptual framework. Because there are as yet few legal restrictions to the practice of what anyone may label "social work," the majority of persons who so designate themselves do not have full professional training, i.e., the equivalent of a two-years Masters degree. The writer strongly urges that this serve as the minimum educational requirement for social workers recruited to attend to the needs of the deaf. For purposes of research work, the social worker with the doctoral degree should be considered.

New Priorities in Deaf Services

What of the tasks that lie ahead, particularly those in which social work can play an effective role? There is no question but that our most productive professional efforts can and should be exerted for the young, to enhance their emotional growth and development, to build their characters, to guide them in establishing firm identities as mature individuals.

Guidance services for parents in dealing with their young deaf children appear grossly insufficient at this time. Whatever the organizational pattern for the provision of such services—whether provided through hospital-based audiological clinics, comprehensive speech and hearing centers, schools, or a combination of facilities—is not as important as an agreement on the basic kinds of needs which we think must be met through such programs. From the social work viewpoint, the needs of the deaf child and his family are often too narrowly and perhaps too mechanically interpreted as physiological problems, educational problems, or resource-planning problems. The social work plea is for consideration of the family as a whole: the impact of deafness on the family, its resources for coping with the handicap both at the point of recognizing the handicap and at critical stages in the child's development. Social work has focused its concern primarily on the handicapped child himself, while insufficient attention has been given to the problems of parents who carry the burden of his rearing. It is probably fair to say that least attention has been given to the long-term process of enabling the family of a deaf child to integrate the handicapped child as fully as possible so that he acquires status, assumes responsibility, and derives role expectations and interactive stimulation to the fullest extent feasible, on a par with other family members. *Understanding the impact of childhood deafness on a family* is critical. Ackerman vividly likens the family

> to a semipermeable membrane, a porous covering sac, which allows a selective interchange between the enclosed members and the outside world. "Reality" seeps through the pores of the sac selectively to affect the enclosed members in a way predetermined by the quality of the sac. . . . Excess tension within the sac arising from a state of imbalance among the enclosed members may warp the sac. Unless balance is restored, the accumulated internal pressure may eventually burst it.[4]

Social work has long been concerned with the principle of homeostasis, that is, the capacity of the individual or family organism to sustain effective, coordinated functioning under constantly changing conditions of life. The essence of life is change; this change requires continuing growth, learning, adaptation to new conditions, and the creative evolution of new levels of interchange between person and environment. In this respect homeostasis cannot be a condition of static balance and security but one of controlled "instability."[4] In their study of adjustment to blindness, Bauman and Yoder conclude that severe parental reactions to the handicapped child are in varying degrees almost inevitable.[5] Westlund and Palumbo suggest that every service for handicapped children should be concerned with, and provide opportunity for, psychiatric help to parents.[6] Introduction of the deaf child into the life stream of a family calls for critical adaptations on the part of family members. Some are able to meet this crisis effectively and creatively. Others meet the challenge with pathological forms of adaption or react to expel the "foreign" body from the family life stream.

It is imperative to obtain an early psychosocial study of the family in order to effectively assist in mobilization of family resources to meet the problems presented by the handicapped child. For some families, the advent of an impaired child constitutes a crises. Recent clinical attention to crisis reactions has produced a body of knowledge and methodologies for remediation, for prevention of chronic problems, and for the development of new capacities. Rapoport postulates that in a state of crisis the habitual problem-solving activities are not adequate for a rapid re-establishment of equilibrium. The event that precipitates the crisis is of such a nature as to require a solution that is new to the individual in relation to his previous life experience. Many individuals are able to develop novel solutions out of their normal range of problem-solving mechanisms and can deal adequately with the hazardous event. Others are unable to respond with appropriate solutions, so that the hazardous event and its sequelae continue to be a source of stress that creates considerable maladaptation.[7]

To summarize: Preparation of the deaf child for family living begins with preparation of the family to live with the child. However, children grow, parental and family needs and relationships change, and periodic readjustments are required. The child encounters critical growth and transition periods with which he and his family often need help. It is even more imperative for the parents of handicapped children to have opportunity for periodic guidance than for the parents of physically normal children. That the communication barriers and maturational lags of deaf children greatly complicate parental handling is too obvious to require elaboration.

Separation of the child from home to attend school—whether day school or residential—is a critical transitional step for both parents and children. Properly handled, so that child and family are able to cope with the anxiety inherent in this transition, the experience becomes one that frees both to mobilize their energies constructively to face new challenges.[8] Improperly handled, the experience may be quite traumatic and may encapsulate anxieties and maladaptive behaviors that continue to be reactivated at points of transition later in life. The present practices of many schools, especially those which physically remove children from their own homes, are potentially quite detrimental to the emotional development of the child. They may well contribute to later difficulties the child encounters in approaching new life experiences.

School placement is merely, however, the initial event and precursor to long years during which parental dominion over the child is shared with and often even abdicated to the school. There are many who have pointed out the uneasy relationship that often exists between family and school. Too frequently schools have viewed the home as a potential competitor and as an unwholesome influence on the child. It is very likely that many of the schools seeking "improved cooperation with parents," in the previously mentioned survey, are primarily interested in parental conformity to school authority.

What should be the relationship between the natural family and the residential school? Traditionally, residential schools for the deaf have endeavored to explain their roles vis-a-vis the family in terms of the boarding school model. That is, the function of the school is primarily educational rather than developmental, and in theory, at least, responsibility for child development remains with the family. Most residential schools would probably no longer subscribe wholly to this theoretical model. Some indeed, have seriously challenged it through their assumption of broader responsibilities for personality and character development of their students. In practice, many deaf children are reared in a parental vacuum.

A child is a growing and developing being; his emotional growth must occur in relationship to meaningful people in his life. Such growth does not and cannot occur in a feeling vacuum.

During the past few years I have had the unusual opportunity to study the child welfare programs of three state residential schools, each long established with a history of stable and qualified administration. In interviews conducted with 22 houseparents, one of the most consistent findings was their spontaneously expressed concern for the gradually declining tie between students and their families as the child's school tenure lengthened. A number of houseparents referred to this condition as a source of acute distress among the children in their care. This condition reflects a universally noted phenomena among children who live away from home, that is, their frequent and intense concern over a felt loss of their families. A related phenomenon readily documented by other types of child-care residences that maintain children for relatively long periods of time is the slow decline in interest in the child on the part of parents who are not strongly motivated to maintain attachments to him or who never had a strong attachment.

Through failure to come to grips with the vital issues of "parenting," many schools fail to assist in deepening familial ties or in supplanting the family through provision of substitutive parenting. After all the years of communications training, with whom and about what is the child supposed to communicate, if he has nothing to say to his family, or they to him? If the only defined parent figures he encounters in his development are an endless procession of houseparents he shares with some 30 other children, with whom does he learn to develop attachments? What adults are to become his models? What conceptions of family living does he bring to his own marriage?

These are not new questions; sensitive educators have struggled with them for many years. However, education for the deaf has generally not established adequate communicational or organizational ties with the mainstream of the child welfare movement and consequently the knowledge and experience available from this source has not been extensively utilized. Parts of the problem—as, for example, the need to upgrade child-care staff—are well recognized, but this partialized approach is generally not viewed within the context of broad child welfare objectives and organizational frameworks. A broader view of the problem would require examination of at least the following areas:

1. Clarification of the role, objectives, and purposes of the deaf school in relation to personality and character development of its students.

2. The role of child care staff and guidelines for implementation of this role, including optimal houseparent-student ratios, qualifications of staff, the role of the houseparent in the staff team, the objectives, duties, and child-management techniques of houseparents.

3. Organizational forms for assuring effective communication between educational staff and child-care staff.

4. Organizational forms for supervision, support, and ongoing training of houseparents.

5. The role of the school in relationship to families of the students and methods for implementation of this role.

6. The need for services to support child-welfare programming: psychiatric, pediatric, psychological, casework, and perhaps other.

7. Organizational forms that invest child-welfare staff with authority to implement their jobs.

Unless and until schools are prepared to commit themselves to education for personal growth and family living and to give serious study to means whereby these objectives can be integrated within the present functions of the organization, the mere addition of casework staff, for example, does little to correct the deeper problems involved. It is the climate for personality growth within schools that should command attention, not isolated parts. It is, for example, extremely difficult to reconcile a school's avowed objective for promoting self-sufficiency with practices that remove from the student any and all opportunity for the very experiences that promote self-sufficiency. It is ironic and unfortunate that classroom teachers must often struggle desperately to coax a minimum of self-assertiveness from their students, whose assertiveness has been all but extinguished by institutional regimentation. It is short-sighted for schools to anticipate the growth of students' sense of responsibility when the climate does not exist in which responsibility normally grows—relationship to adults one wants to please, participation in determining at least part of what one must do and be, opportunity for some assertion against authority, the necessity for struggling with the results of one's freely made decisions.

To a large extent these are conditions of choice rather than necessity. Philosophies and systems have long been established for the operation of group-care milieus that are child-centered rather than program-centered. Sensitive, knowledgeable, effective, child-care staff can be developed. Environments that allow for the growth of self-sufficiency, self-assertiveness, curiosity, and individuality can also effectively carry out educational objectives.

Access is available to the highest standards of group care for children, and I most urgently recommend the consideration of such standards. The resource is the Child Welfare League of America (CWLA), founded in 1920 to improve services for children that support, supplement, or substitute for parental care and supervision. It is the only national, privately supported organization devoting its efforts completely to child welfare. It operates as a federation of 265 member agencies, sectarian and non-sectarian, private and public, contributing to the development of standards for its membership,[9] making available its highly competent field staff, helping agencies to organize their resources to carry out the objectives for children which they want to achieve. Consultative services are available to deaf schools for a fee. The League can serve as one vehicle for schools seriously interested in gaining insight and new approaches to progressive child care and training.

If the burden of these remarks seems to fall on the state-supported deaf schools, this is only because of their pre-eminent role in deaf education. What has been said applies equally, of course, to the private residential school. Public and private day schools have also failed to make the leadership in preventive mental health that has been open to them. At this stage in the development of services to the deaf it is unfortunately true that virtually no other resources exist to support the schools in their mental health role so that full responsibility does fall on the shoulders of these institutions. The professional service area that can be most fruitful for both day and residential schools, all of which must set priorities based on limited time and resources, is that of group education and group counseling for parents. If families can be effectively mobilized to collaborate with schools around educational, social, and personality objectives for the child, the children may benefit enormously. Currently schools undertake to teach social living skills that can, in my estimation, be effectively taught best within the living context of the family and the community.

Sensitive educators have long been aware, for example, that home economics training in cooking does not become a living reality until it is practiced, under normal life conditions, in a family kitchen. They are quite aware that no amount of academic preparation in the economic realities of purchasing can, *per se*, adequately prepare a youngster for tasks which must ultimately be carried out by the individual alone, confronting the realities of the situation. Many families may need guidance in translating to the home and community those skills which are being initiated at school. Many families will require ongoing opportunities for obtaining from the school the insights that can be gleaned from teachers or child-care staff. Schools likewise need to obtain from the home the insights of parents. School staff that is divorced from communication with the student's family and community life forces the student to split off his two worlds more sharply than necessary.

Professional casework and group work have developed a considerable body of techniques, out of experience with parent groups and family-school intercommunication, that can be of significant value for integrating the child's world into an effective whole.

The planners of this conference have urged speakers to address themselves to the point of interdisciplinary planning and coordination. The one recommendation I would make, in the time allotted, is that the discipline of psychiatric medicine find access to the study of "normal" phenomena among the deaf rather than relegating itself essentially to the treatment (little as there is of this) of severe pathology. Ideally every school and service program should have available psychiatric consultation. Psychiatric knowledge has a potentially vital contribution to make to the understanding of many individual and group phenomena with which all of us are presently struggling.

Whatever I may have said of a critical nature grows out of a basic respect for the dedication and integrity of my colleagues in service to the deaf, who are deeply interested in constructive change. I trust that I have been a coherent and constructive critic. I hope that others in social work will be encouraged to participate in the challenges ahead.

REFERENCES

1. Rainer, J. D. and Kallmann, F. J.: Preventive mental health planning. In *Family and Mental Health Problems in a Deaf Population* (Rainer, J. D., Altshuler, K. Z. and Kallmann, F. J., eds.). New York State Psychiatric Institute, New York, 1963.

2. Bartlett, H. M.: Toward clarification and improvement of social work practice. *Social Work, 3:* 3, 1958.

3. Bartlett, H. M.: The place and use of knowledge in social work practice. *Social Work, 9:* 36, 1964.

4. Ackerman, N. W.: *The Psychodynamics of Family Life.* Basic Books, New York, 1958.

5. Bauman, M. K. and Yoder, N. N.: *Adjustment to Blindness—Reviewed.* Charles C. Thomas, Springfield, Ill., 1966.

6. Westlund, N. and Palumbo, A.: Parental rejection of crippled children. *Am. J. Orthopsychiat., 16:* 271, 1946.

7. Rapoport, L.: Working with families in crisis: an exploration in preventive intervention. *Social Work, 7:* 49, 1962.

8. Anderson, W. C., Orentstein, D. F., Lake, D. and Hersh, A.: Separation used to help parents promote growth in their retarded child. *Social Work, 9:* 60, 1964.

9. CWLA standards for residential group care of children were established in 1963; they appear in the document, *Child Welfare League of America—Standards for Services of Child Welfare Institutions.*

Mental Health for the Deaf in the School Setting

WILLIAM J. McCLURE

PRIOR to the 16th century, history has little to say about education of the deaf, and only a few teachers are mentioned during the following 150 years. Through the Middle Ages the deaf were generally considered incapable of receiving an education and incompetent to manage their affairs. While early teachers had proved that individual deaf pupils could benefit from instruction, the first schools for the deaf did not appear until about the 1760's when such schools were established in France, Germany, and Scotland. The first permanent schools for the deaf in this country were established between 1817 and 1820 in Hartford, Connecticut, New York City, and Philadelphia. A hundred and fifty years later, every state provides for the education of its deaf children through both public and private residential schools, day schools, and day classes. According to the May 1967 issue of the *American Annals of the Deaf*, 35,943 children are enrolled in these schools, with a total educational staff of 6,535, of whom 5,528 are classroom teachers.

Professional association and interaction with other disciplines has been late in coming to educators of the deaf. This could be due to the comparatively small numbers of the deaf and of educators of the deaf. Perhaps the honest, though intense, differences of opinion that educators of the deaf have had concerning methods of communication and of instruction have caused them to avoid contact with other disciplines. They have tried to keep these differences "in the family," perhaps for fear that exposure to the light of research or to examination by others would destroy opinions which have been held with almost missionary zeal. Fortunately, times are changing and educators of the deaf are in contact with professionals from many disciplines. Today deafness is being discussed, studied, and researched from many points of view.

This conference on Mental Health Services for Deaf Persons is another step forward. We who work with deaf children have long envied

New York State its mental health program of services for the deaf, and have wished that considerations of finance and distance did not preclude our referring deaf children and their parents to that center when we see evidence of maladjustment and excessive frustration. This meeting should help to disseminate some of the knowledge acquired by the New York group and should point the way toward better mental health services for the deaf in the future.

Let me begin by pointing out some of the problems which arise in schools for the deaf, which seem to indicate the need for psychiatric services—possibly a cooperative relationship between our schools and a psychiatric service center. In any educational program for deaf children truly adequate services will eventually require close cooperation with representatives of many disciplines.

Some of my fellow educators occasionally accuse me of being unduly pessimistic. I could, to be sure, mention the federal assistance now available to help recruit and train teachers of the deaf, the workshops and meetings which enable educators to exchange ideas among themselves, and those which involve other disciplines, such as this one. It seems more constructive however, in the long run, to explain our needs and our problems to others who can help toward an eventual solution, rather than to paint rosy pictures and then go home to cry in private about our continuing shortcomings.

The changing population in schools for the deaf has created problems. Forty years ago two-fifths of our pupils had acquired language and communication ability before becoming deaf.[1, 2] There is today much less adventitious deafness. Cases which do occur usually remain in the public schools, as they should, often in special classes for the hard of hearing. This leaves schools for the deaf with a very different type of pupil to serve. Now, approximately 90 percent of the children are much more difficult to educate. Methods of instruction in the majority of schools for the deaf have not adapted to this changing population. Consequently, a larger percentage of pupils are frustrated by methods of communication designed for the hard of hearing and the adventitiously deaf. Deafness is a handicap primarily because of its effect on communication and on the development of language and speech. For the child without hearing, vision must be the principal avenue of learning. More deaf than hearing fail to reach their educational potential. This failure undoubtedly contributes to frustration and possible maladjustment. The average I.Q. for the deaf is not significantly different from that of those who hear, even though deafness of certain etiologies may be accompanied by multiple handicaps.[3]

The employment status of the deaf population is at variance with what one would expect from an assessment of intelligence. According to the Report of the National Advisory Committee on Education of the Deaf,[2] five-sixths of the deaf adults are manual laborers of varying skills compared with one-half of the hearing population. Only 17 percent of the deaf population are employed in white collar jobs compared to 46.8

percent of the general U. S. population.[4,5] There is a high correlation between educational achievement and the level of work and income. The proportion of deaf students able to gain college entrance is only one tenth of one percent of those with normal hearing who are admitted to college.[6] The Babbidge Report points out that the average graduate of a public residential school for the deaf—the closest we have to generally available high schools for the deaf—has an 8th-grade education. As we will see later, this "average" graduate does not include the students who leave without a diploma. Obviously, existing educational programs do not enable the majority of deaf students to attain their potential. This undoubtedly results in excessive frustration for many of the deaf.

The Babbidge Report goes on to say:

> This unsatisfactory state of education of the deaf cannot be attributed to any lack of dedication on the part of those who teach and work with the deaf. The basic explanation lies in our failure to launch an aggressive assault on some of the basic problems of language learning . . . and in our failure to develop a more systematic and adequate program for educating the deaf at all levels.[2]

Schools for the deaf need professionals, including psychiatrists, in strengthening total educational programs.

The findings of the Babbidge Committee are borne out by two extensive studies, one by Marshall S. Hester, former superintendent of the New Mexico School for the Deaf and the other by E. B. Boatner, superintendent of the American School for the Deaf at West Hartford, Connecticut.

In his paper on manual communication given at the International Congress on Education of the Deaf in 1963,[7] Dr. Hester reported a survey of the achievement test scores of 1,104 pupils age 16 and up, who left schools for the deaf during the 1961-62 school year. These were from 55 residential and 9 day schools or classes in the United States. There were 501 graduates and 603 non-graduates, age 16 and older, in 1962. Remember, "graduates" does not mean graduates of a high school but of a program offered in a school for the deaf, often terminating at the 8th-, 9th- or 10th-grade level. As measured on achievement tests, the 501 graduates ranged from 3.1 to 12.8 grade level. The median was 8.1, the mean was 7.9. The 603 non-graduates had a grade range of .9 to 10.5. The median for this group was 4.7, as was the mean. In other words, the average student completing his education in our system of elementary and secondary schools for the deaf in 1962 had an achievement level somewhere between 6th and 7th grade. Half of all deaf students leaving school ranked below this level. Since it is not customary for schools of this kind to serve children who are mentally retarded or those who have serious learning problems the achievement is woefully low, considering the educational potential.

In October 1964,[8] Dr. Boatner made a similar survey of 16-year-old school leavers. He included all of the 67 public residential schools, the 15 day schools, and 17 denominational and private schools. He received replies from 88 schools representing 93 percent of the enrollment in all special programs for the deaf in the United States. They reported 1,277 leavers. There were 1,145 leavers from residential schools; of these, 449, with a Stanford average of 8.2, received academic diplomas; 339 with a Stanford average of 5.3, received vocational certificates, and attendance certificates were given to 150. Two hundred and eight left school without any type of certificate. From the day schools and denominational and private schools there were 132 leavers; of these 81 received academic diplomas (Stanford average, 7.3), vocational certificates were given to 14 with an average of 5.0, and 37 left with only attendance certificates or no certificates at all. Of the 1,277 leavers reported by the 88 schools, only 70 obtained a 10th grade Stanford test average or better. Sixty-five of these were from residential schools, five from private schools. None were reported from the day schools. No figures were given on the 297 day classes for the deaf, as they rarely retain pupils to the age of 16. In view of the normal intelligence of most of the deaf, this educational failure is both puzzling and frustrating.

Undoubtedly the chief cause for poor achievement in schools for the deaf is language deficiency. We know the difficulty of trying to learn a foreign language when we have hearing to help us and our mother tongue to use as a crutch. Imagine the difficulty encountered by deaf children who must learn language by *visual means alone* without the benefit of another language upon which to lean. The ages of 2-4 are most critical of language acquisition. What is needed is an acceptable, clearly visible method of communication to adequately provide the young deaf child with a better means of early language development.

At the 1959 meeting of the American Instructors of the Deaf, Dr. Edgar Lowell, Administrator of the John Tracy Clinic, reported an experiment in the use of speechreading and its relationship to language development.[9] On a "film test of lipreading" Dr. Lowell and his associates found that deaf students at the high school level understood only 25.7 percent of the material presented to them. Hearing students on the same level, without instruction in lipreading, understood by lipreading 37.6 percent. At the college level, deaf students understood 44.9 percent and hearing students 51.6 percent. Teachers of the deaf scored best of all on this test of lipreading ability, with the deaf teachers of the deaf scoring 67.9 percent and the hearing teachers of the deaf scoring 57.1 percent. Deaf teachers of the deaf are often, of course, selected both for their ability to instruct and also because they have achieved, for deaf persons, an outstanding ability to communicate with the hearing world. If the deaf high school student understands only 25 percent of the material presented to him through lipreading, what must the level be for the deaf child who has not yet reached high school level or age? A child who understands less than half of what is presented to him by lipreading is at a tremendous disadvantage in acquiring an education, if lipreading is the principal method of communication. Imagine the frustrations encountered in such a context, and the implications for social adjustment and mental health. A more visible and facile system of communication needs to be found, which is acceptable to all. Perhaps psychiatrists can help us solve this problem.

There are many valid reasons for the belief that residential schools for the deaf contribute to the adjustment of the deaf child by giving him a feeling of acceptance. He identifies with a group having needs, abilities, disabilities, and problems similar to his own. He is a part of an "in group" and from this gains emotional support and security. Much has been said about the values of residential programs for deaf children as opposed to the day-class programs. With the low prevalence of deafness, it is virtually impossible to establish educational programs within commuting distance of every child's home. There is also the consideration of family ability to handle the problems of deafness. If the family cannot adjust to the deaf child, provide the warmth, the educational support, and the management the child needs, then residential programs deserve strong consideration regardless of the proximity of day programs.[3]

Sometimes residential schools are unable to handle certain types of behavior because of the effect on other pupils. The following letter illustrates the type of problem with which schools would like to have the assistance of experts. It illustrates also the need for better mental health services. The names, of course, have been altered.

Dear Mr. and Mrs. Jones:

I was truly sorry to have to call and tell you that we were having serious difficulties with John, and that we would have to send him home. There was, however, no alternative since on the evening before he had 1) kicked his houseparent, 2) thrown a large rock at another boy, 3) bitten two boys on the arms so severely that both boys had to be treated at the infirmary.

Temper outbursts such as John has manifested cannot be ignored or tolerated. We must think of the health and safety of all the children in our care. Our parents must feel reasonably certain that their children's welfare and safety are in good hands and well guarded.

It might be wise for you to have John's physical and mental condition checked. Perhaps there is some physiological or psychological reason for these temper outbursts. I certainly hope some cause can be determined and treated so that we might be assured that his actions will not be detrimental to the health of others here at school, should he return.

We expect to move into a new dormitory in the near future, which will give opportunity to divide children into smaller groups under closer supervision. If, after we have moved and are well settled, we find that circumstances will permit giving John another trial, we will get in touch with you. In the meantime, we would suggest that you seek professional help.

Sincerely yours,

Parents often cannot understand why a group of adults cannot control a recalcitrant 10-, 11-, or 12-year-old boy or girl. They do not understand the difficulties of giving individual attention, when houseparents are responsible for groups of 15 to 20, and sometimes, 25 to 30 children. They also do not understand the effect that one difficult child can have on the behavior and adjustment of the others in the group—not to mention the difficulty of retaining houseparents when such behavior cannot be controlled.

Another instance of behavior which was totally inexplicable to school personnel was that of a 15-year-old boy who persisted in puncturing five-gallon cans of paint-thinner which were kept in the vocational department. The cans would be cleverly punctured from below and the paint thinner would slowly leak out, gradually saturating the racks, the floor, and the area around. This was, of course, a highly combustible situation. Despite every effort to reprimand and restrain the boy, this behavior could not be prevented. Consequently, it was necessary to send him home.

Often this same boy would simply refuse to go to school and would hide out in the dormitory. It was not unusual to find him stretched out at full length on one of the higher shelves in a closet. The boy was not particularly difficult to control in his relations with other children, and it was the obsession to create hazardous situations that led to his dismissal. School officials realized they needed the help of psychiatrists, but unfortunately such help was not available.

The Research Conference on Behavioral Aspects of Deafness[10] perceived the deficiency of verbal interaction between the deaf child and his family as a paramount consideration warranting additional research. The conference also speculated about the different interaction of *deaf* parents and *deaf* siblings with the young deaf child, compared to the relationship of *hearing* parents and *hearing* siblings with the deaf child. The feeling was that the school for the deaf plays a major role in establishing patterns of adjustment in deaf students. A tendency seems to exist to shift the major responsibility for the general care of the deaf child from the family to the school, and particularly to residential schools. The recent Workshop on Extending Mental Health Services to the Deaf,[11] also noted the deaf child's greater dependence on the school. It was suggested that schools take steps to involve the family in the educational process and to encourage the deaf child to identify strongly with his family group. The curriculum also should assist the deaf student in understanding his environment and his role within it, with particular emphasis on personal initiative and independence of action. In view of the problems deaf persons have in sexual adjustment and family life,[12, 13] a more satisfactory approach in instruction on the part of schools should help to lessen the incidence of such problems. For many years schools for the deaf even more than public schools have carefully avoided the subject of sex education or preparation for family life. The schools until recently have said in essence, "This is the parent's responsibility," despite their knowledge that parents were inadequately prepared for such responsibility. Now they are beginning to examine their own responsibilities more thoroughly and carefully, and a number of schools for the deaf are instituting courses in this area. Materials and suggestions for sex education have recently been developed at the Illinois School for the Deaf[14] and also at a recent workshop on Sex Education, under auspices of the U. S. Office of Education.[15] These materials have recently been made available to schools for the deaf over the country.

One reason contributing to the hesitance of schools for the deaf and parents of deaf children in tackling problems of sex education, or even in answering the queries of deaf children, has been the children's extreme language limitations, and the embarrassment attendant upon the use of signs, gestures, and pantomime when dealing with such subjects. Deaf children would seem to require a sufficient mastery of the language necessary to understand the answers before such answers are given them.

A number of studies suggest that persons who are totally deaf may make better adjustments than the hard-of-hearing because they know they cannot hear, and unlike the hard-of-hearing, do not have to worry about the limits of their ability to communicate through the auditory process. This does not mean that the totally deaf person in all instances has made the appropriate adjustment to get along with those in the hearing world, but rather that he is in a better position to make such an adjustment because he accepts his hearing deficiency and relies upon techniques that do not require the auditory process. Therefore he does not face the problems of "marginality" which characterize the hard-of-hearing person who fluctuates between the world of the deaf and the world of the hearing. The deaf person is not plagued with the ambiguous role of the hard-of-hearing person who can never be sure in advance if he can perform in a particular social situation because limitations he must accept are relatively undefined.[10] . . .

Sussman introduced us to the term "marginality,"[16] generally referred to in literature on race and nationality relations to describe the individual who belongs to two cultural worlds. Not being wholly part of either world, the person is comfortable in neither. He is on the edge both socially and psychologically. This aptly describes the plight of many deaf children who are told again and again that they *can* adjust and fit well into the world of the hearing. When this does not develop as expected, they can become frustrated and confused, and sometimes they withdraw from both groups.

Sussman also pointed to studies showing that profoundly deaf youngsters tend to make better school adjustments than the hard-of-hearing, and that their adjustment levels are not too different from those of a control group of hearing adolescents. His conclusion was that the condition itself is not as upsetting as the marginality of the individual.[16] The President of the National Association of the Deaf has also stated that "isolation of the deaf person is never so complete as when he rejects deaf society and is rejected by the hearing society because he cannot (except in exceedingly rare cases) compete."[17]

Educators of the deaf have long urged that the viewpoints of intelligent leaders from state and national associations for the deaf be considered in developing educational and vocational programs. This point of view gained valuable support recently when Edna S. Levine and the new Center for Research and Training at New York University sponsored the first institute for deaf professional persons. *The Deaf American* said about the institute,

> The deaf adult has been a relative "unknown" in educational thinking. As the net product of special education, the deaf adult represents the ultimate testing ground for present educational, vocational, developmental, psychological, and other theories. It should not come as any surprise that the deaf adult population may be the most fruitful resource of answers and solutions to the many unsolved questions and problems in the education and rehabilitation of the deaf. Today's deaf adult can tell us much about yesterday's attempts to aid him. By exploring and serving the needs of this group and by tapping this reservoir of information and experiences, we may ultimately come to a better and more realistic understanding of deafness and the deaf. Thus, the shifting of attention to the deaf adult person today is a very timely step.[18]

As emphasized by Sussman,[16] it is quite possible that our knowledge about the deaf and their problems is deficient because we use a frame of reference fitted to the world of hearing. Intent on doing the "right" thing (by our lights), we may not seriously attempt to find out what the deaf people themselves really want. While every deaf person cannot automatically know the solution to his problems, the consensus among able leaders of the deaf population should not be ignored.

It is regrettable that those who could offer so much are seldom consulted by the people attempting to solve their problems. The blind struggled for more than a hundred years for the Braille system which enables them to read. Sighted people opposed the idea, ignoring the views of the blind themselves and claiming that the blind should learn to read raised printed letters that were copies of the letters that sighted people use. Finally a blind man, Louis Braille, found influential friends who would listen to him and help him develop the Braille System. A similar breakthrough, whereby the hearing would help the deaf to gain acceptance for the methods they, the deaf, feel most beneficial for their own welfare, would be a boon for the deaf.

Schools for the deaf and psychiatrists need to exert their joint influence for the adjustment and well-being of the deaf through realistic parent education and guidance. Parents at the beginning usually have little understanding of the educational implications of deafness. They are impressed by the inability of their children to speak, rather than the lack of hearing. They are prone to interpret statements that their child will learn to speak as a promise to fluent speech, and they ignore—or prefer not to recognize—that the primary problem is that of developing a command of language. Delighted with the limited speech and language of the primary grades, they erroneously assume that the older deaf people whom they have difficulty in understanding did not have similar training. Persons in early contact with parents do a disservice to both deaf children and their parents when they fail to give *complete and accurate* information on the deaf child's need for acceptance and for an early and accurate *two-way* system of communication.

More emotional trauma is probably generated over the teaching, acquisition, and use of speech than over any other facet of a deaf child's education. In his doctoral dissertation on the subject, Schunhoff predicts,

> The teaching of speech will continue to be the most difficult activity in the curriculum and proponents of the oral method should ever be mindful not to mislead parents into thinking all deaf children can acquire fluent, natural speech. Speech teaching will always be difficult and there will be varying degrees of success.[19]

Fuller seems to echo these sentiments when he says,

> There seem to me to be many parents of deaf children whose determination to teach their children to talk is so strange that it distorts their sense of educational perspective. In terms of his ultimate school achievement it is probably more important that your child learn to read than that he learn to speak, and this tends to be true too for the child with normal hearing. The minimum objectives of an educational program are to develop those skills which will enable each person to become economically independent as an adult and to acquaint him sufficiently well with our social customs and statutory laws so that he will not flout the one or violate the other. These are the bare essentials, and speech is not necessary for either. This level of educational achievement is far exceeded by most deaf adults who do not talk. Speech is desirable for all deaf people and our schools should make every effort to teach it, but it should not bulk so large in our ambitions for the deaf child that we lose sight of his other educational needs.[20]

Regarding social competence and emotional stability, Fuller also comments:

> The mere fact that hearing people can talk does not seem to save them from social inadequacy or from emotional confusions. There is no evidence to indicate that speech is any more effective in promoting social maturity or emotional stability in deaf people than it is among the hearing. Indeed, there is every reason to believe that good speech is a result of emotional maturity rather than a cause of it.[20]

Given accurate information and an opportunity to objectively view the probable results, parents will have a better understanding of the communication and educational hurdles that confront their deaf children. With a fuller comprehension of their needs and those of their child, they may constructively initiate efforts to meet these needs and so develop healthy mental attitudes in the child.

As a prelude to cooperating on a project with the University of Illinois Institute for Research on Exceptional Children a few years ago, I interviewed the parents of all children entering the Indiana School for the Deaf in 1965 and 1966. The purpose of the interview was to explain the research project to the parents and to request permission to use their children in the experimental fingerspelling classes, provided the children met the requirements of age, intelligence, and degree of hearing loss. After the project was explained, only one of the more than 90 families objected to a child's being considered. The objection was on the valid basis that this particular child had a considerable amount of residual hearing. Later, other parents throughout the school were so impressed with the progress of these classes and with the family rapport, that the Parent-Teacher-Counselor Organization, with the help of a grant from the Vocational Rehabilitation Administration, established fingerspelling classes for parents and friends of deaf children throughout the state. In 1965-66 over 600 attended these classes. A second grant was secured for the 1966-67 school year and again enrollment was over 600.

The difference in the attitude of the children was remarkable when they found that their parents were attending classes in fingerspelling. It was not uncommon for them to proudly inform classmates that *their* parents cared enough to learn to communicate with them. Though difficult to assess, the resultant increase in strength of family ties and in family solidarity and understanding is indisputable.

Parents also felt that they gained a greater ease of communication with the deaf friends and classmates of their children. This, in turn, helped the children to feel that their friends were accepted and understood in the family circle. Before, many families had been ill at ease around deaf people other than their own children, and the parental acceptance of a child and his friends was another positive force in the development of health-building parental attitudes.

I believe that these parents have learned much about their children's need for emotional support and for a means of communication which can help them become accepted and participating members of the family group. Parents need the reassurance of psychiatrists, among others, in courageously attacking the problem of effective communication along these lines.

Parents have often come to me with the request, "Tell my child (something)." When I express surprise, parents explain that they were told, when the child was young, never to communicate except by speech and lipreading. As the child grew older the parent and child were often unable to communicate in other than short, uncertain phrases and sentences. I have had mothers tell me they have never had a satisfactory mother-daughter teenage talk. This is tragic! What can schools do to prevent this from occurring? Better advice to parents, including a clear explanation of the children's special need for acceptance as they are, and the pressing need to communicate, would obviously result in stronger family relationships.

As Mary Jane Rhodes emphasized in *The Deaf American:*

In thinking about my first column, I decided to write what I would like to say to parents who have just been advised that their child is deaf. If we could only reach these parents when they have first become aware of their child's handicap, we could save them years of heartache and frustration.

After 14 years of living with a deaf child, my first bit of advice to any parent of a deaf child would be to understand and accept his deafness as a handicap of communication. . . .

Next, I would tell parents: Don't be confused by the communications-methods controversy. Since deafness is a handicap of communication you are unfair to your child unless you use when necessary every method of communication available to the deaf. These methods include gestures, the language of signs, fingerspelling, writing, speech, speechreading, and drawing pictures. When you choose to use only one method of communication with your child, you deprive him of many opportunities to express himself. Our deaf citizens will assure you that they want and need every method of communication available to them. Don't confuse home communication with school communication. Use whatever method of communication you need at home to share your family life with your deaf child.

. . . Give him an extra share of physical affection and it will be much easier for you to correct him when it is necessary. Love is the easiest of all methods of communication, so don't be afraid to use lots of it and often.

My next bit of advice can make the difference between a well-adjusted deaf child and a misfit who will not, who can not adjust to his world of silence, so please be proud of your deaf child.[21]

Later, she restated the case:

The audiologist, psychologist, or educator of the deaf, who advises parents never to consider the use of other than oral communication with their deaf child is practically sentencing that child to a life of loneliness and maladjustment. Deafness need not be the handicap that it is today. Pure oralism may have been a legitimate goal in the days when handicapped children were hidden or protected from the public. Now all handicaps are accepted and public education campaigns are in progress to explain the effects of various handicaps. . . . Now is the time to accept and to publicize all methods of communication for the deaf. Until we hearing mothers and fathers accept and use a facile method of communication with our deaf children we hearing parents are our deaf child's greatest handicap![21]

Newman agrees when he says, regarding mental health and communication:

Frustration resulting from lack of communication is one of the greatest contributions to poor mental health. At the California School for the Deaf in Riverside, there are many examples of children coming in from oral environments who are continuously tense and upset.

After there is ease of communication, many but not all relax and their emotional health improves. Some come too late and the damage is irrevocably done.

He concludes,

The deaf are resourceful people and are capable of assimilating different methods and of shifting from one method to another. Perhaps, soon, a breath of fresh air will enter our field with all findings on how the deaf learn, based on scientific research. Only then could be ushered in an age of tolerance and enlightment.[22]

Too many parents fail to realize the effect that very small things can have on the attitude of the deaf child, or on the attitude of the deaf person towards himself. I have had students tell of their frustrations when parents would send them to the grocery store together with a younger sibling, and the money was given to the younger, but hearing child. The deaf child inevitably feels his parents do not trust him, do not believe he can assume responsibility, and relegate him to a subordinate position. Stop and consider what effect this type of treatment can have on the deaf child, adolescent, or adult.

Parents influence greatly the psychological adjustment of their deaf children. If parents accept the deafness realistically, and understand and interpret its implications correctly, the child will accept and adjust to his deafness. Parents who do not accept the child as he is, lead him to perceive himself as rejected.

Too few physicians, psychologists, and psychiatrists are capable of counselling with parents who have just learned that their child is deaf. This responsibility has been ignored or thrust upon schools and educators who need the assistance of other professionals in order to give parents a full measure of understanding.

Some time ago I talked with a deaf teacher at the Indiana School for the Deaf. It was her feeling that deaf children now are even more likely to be retarded and frustrated than they were when she was growing up. She felt that this was so because today hearing children pick up a great deal of language and incidental information from radio and television sources which are not available to the deaf child. Years ago, hearing children had only the stimulation of actual conversation and communication with the adults around them. Now their experiences have been broadened, while those of the deaf children have remained static. Perhaps the deaf child receives even less stimulation at home than before, because his family may be so engrossed in TV that they take even less time to communicate with him. It is no wonder, then, that so many deaf children and adults develop undesirable behavior patterns.

Schools for the deaf should recognize the responsibility of helping parents to bridge this communication gap rapidly by encouraging multimethod and multimedia approaches. The help of professionals from other disciplines is necessary to convince parents of this need. There is also a need for research on how to accomplish the task most effectively and on how best to reach the parents of very young deaf children. At present, few state- or even community-wide programs exist. A few parents are reached through correspondence courses or through parent workshops, but these are a very small portion of the population and they are often given only one side of the picture. Educators of the deaf may despair of influencing the parents of young children to grasp the difficulties ahead, and may resignedly go through the same cycle with parents, time after time. A combination of forces is necessary, whereby educators, intelligent deaf adults, audiologists, speech and hearing therapists, sociologists, psychologists, psychiatrists, and others who come in touch with the deaf child will insist on the acceptance of reality and on a flexibility of communication methods which will reach the great majority of deaf children. This should be done even while research continues to attempt to find better ways of teaching all that the deaf child should master.

Speaking before the American Psychiatric Association, Sharoff made some observations pertinent to this problem.[23] He pointed out that in their enthusiasm for teaching speech and lipreading to deaf children, some schools prohibited parents from communicating with their child and deaf students from communicating with each other by any means other than oral. He noted that the deaf child would be likely to withdraw more and more from contacts and association with hearing people if he is forced to depend only on oral speech and lipreading. As an illustration he remarked on the transformation that occurs when a deaf child, attempting to become a part of a group of hearing children, is approached by another deaf child:

> It is as if the child suddenly comes to life. The eyes and face light up. There is a change from a human being who is fairly quiet and somewhat perplexed to a vibrant, communicating, live personality. Suddenly there is so much to say with gestures, signs, face, and body that one senses that the child now feels that he will be understood and responded to in an understandable manner. One senses in watching this scene that with the advent of another person with whom the child can communicate life takes on a different meaning.

Tervoort was impressed by this same transformation.[24] Can this obvious benefit of clear communication be overlooked in planning for the mental health of deaf children?

Parents need to know of the increasing body of evidence which points out the advantages for deaf children when all forms of communication are utilized.[2, 3, 7, 9, 10, 11, 19, 20, 23, 24, 25-39]

There is no evidence of an adverse effect on speech and lipreading abilities, and there is some evidence that these are benefited; there are also indications of better overall communication ability, school achievement, and personal adjustment, both within the family and in other situations. Experience leads me to believe that a strong cooperative effort on the part of educators, schools for the deaf, and psychiatrists would help parents of deaf children create a better climate for mental health through acceptance of the child and his handicap.

Underemployment is another major life-problem which creates frustrations for many deaf people. Because of their mobility and intelligence, and their school background of considerable prevocational and vocational shop training, most deaf people find employment quite readily; more often than not, however, the employment is at a level sharply below their ability and capacity.

Additional opportunities are becoming available for secondary and higher educational programs for deaf people. A National Technical Institute for the Deaf has been authorized in connection with Rochester Institute of Technology in Rochester, New York. The objective of this institute is to provide young deaf adults with a wide choice of technical training to enable them to fit into today's working world and to compete with their hearing peers for more challenging technical occupations. Congress has also authorized a model high school for the deaf which will be established in conjunction with Gallaudet College in Washington, D. C. These opportunities for advanced study should help to alleviate some of the present vocational frustrations of deaf people.

In considering educational programs for the deaf and their relationship to mental health, for good or ill, the following points should be kept in mind:

1. The changing population in schools for deaf children.

2. The failure of schools to make it possible for deaf children to achieve their educational potentials.

3. The rising evidence that new, multimedia approaches to teaching language are necessary to erase this failure.

4. The fact that earlier and more fluent communication is essential not only to academic success but to the mental health of the deaf child.

5. The possibility that residential schools may provide a better mental health climate than day schools for the deaf.

6. The necessity of consulting the adult deaf population about programs involving them.

7. The responsibility of psychiatrists and other professionals in contact with deaf children and their parents, along with that of the school, to explain to parents the child's urgent need for acceptance as he is, and his need for effective communication by any means, when necessary.

8. The probability that chronic underemployment as a source of poor mental health in the deaf population may be alleviated by better early education and new programs of advanced education.

REFERENCES

1. Best, H.: *Deafness and the Deaf in the United States.* Macmillan, New York, 1943.

2. Babbidge, H.: *Education of the Deaf.* U. S. Department of Health, Education, and Welfare, Washington, D. C., 1965.

3. Vernon, M. and Mindel, E.: Psychological aspects of profound hearing loss. In *Audiological Assessment* (D. Rose, ed.). Prentice Hall, New Jersey, in press.

4. Crammatte, A. B.: *The Formidable Peak: A Study of Deaf People in Professional Employment*. Gallaudet College, Washington, D. C., 1965.

5. Lunde, A. S. and Bigman, S. K.: *Occupational Conditions Among the Deaf*. Gallaudet College, Washington, D. C., 1959.

6. Schein, J. D. and Bushnaq, S. M.: Higher education of the deaf in the United States: A retrospective investigation. *Amer. Ann. Deaf, 96:* 416, 1962.

7. Hester, M. S.: Manual communication. *Proceedings of the International Congress on Education of the Deaf*. U. S. Government Printing Office, Washington, D. C., 1963.

8. Boatner, E. B.: A Survey Conducted by the Vocational Educational Committee of the Conference on Executives of American Schools for the Deaf, 1964. (unpublished paper).

9. Lowell, E. A.: Research in speechreading: some relationships to language development and implications for the classroom teacher. *Proceedings of the 39th Meeting of the Convention of American Instructors of the Deaf*. U. S. Government Printing Office, Washington, D. C., 1960.

10. Stuckless, E. R., (ed.): *Research on Behavioral Aspects of Deafness*. U. S. Department of Health, Education, and Welfare, Washington, D. C., 1966.

11. Rainer, J. D. and Altshuler, K. Z., (eds.): *Psychiatry and the Deaf*. Proceedings of the Workshop for Psychiatrists on Extending Mental Health Services to the Deaf, April 7-8, 1967. U. S. Dept. of Health, Education, and Welfare, Washington, D. C., 1968.

12. Rainer, J. D., Altshuler, K. Z., Kallmann, F. J. and Deming, W. E. (eds.): *Family and Mental Health Problems in a Deaf Population*. New York State Psychiatric Institute, New York, 1963.

13. Rainer, J. D.: Interpretation, communication and understanding. *The Deaf American, 19:* 43, 1966.

14. Withrow, F.: Personal communication.

15. *Sex Education, Grades K through 12*. Workshop for Improving Instruction for the Deaf. U. S. Department of Health, Education, and Welfare, Washington, D. C., 1965.

16. Sussman, M. B.: Sociological theory and deafness: Problems and prospects. In *Research on Behavioral Aspects of Deafness* (E. R. Stuckless, ed.). U. S. Department of Health, Education, and Welfare, Washington, D. C., 1966.

17. Schreiber, F. C.: National Association of the Deaf, President's Message. *The Deaf American, 20:* 12, 1967.

18. Brauer-Sachs, B. and Sussman, A.: Institute of Deaf Professional Persons—A pioneering endeavor. *The Deaf American, 19:* 15, 1967.

19. Schunhoff, H. F.: *The Teaching of Speech and by Speech in Public Residential Schools for the Deaf in the United States, 1815-1955*. West Virginia School for the Deaf and the Blind, Romney, West Virginia, 1957.

20. Fuller, C. F.: *Your Child, Maturity and You: A Talk with Parents.* Adapted from lectures given to various groups of parents of deaf children in Indiana and Tennessee. Reprinted at the Indiana School for the Deaf, Indianapolis, 1963.

21. Rhodes, M. J.: From a parent's point of view. *The Deaf American, 19:* 14, 1967.

22. Newman, L.: A critical evaluation of Dr. Breunig's paper "Greater Expectations for the Deaf." *The Deaf American, 19:* 17, 1967.

23. Sharoff, R. L.: Enforced restrictions of communication; Its implications for the emotional and intellectual development of the deaf child. *Am. J. Psychiat., 116:* 443, 1959.

24. Tervoort, B. T. and Verbork, A. J. A.: *Analysis of Communicative Structure Patterns in Deaf Children.* U. S. Department of Health, Education, and Welfare, Washington, D. C., 1967.

25. Benson, R. M.: Focus on Children. *The Deaf American, 17:* 12, 1965.

26. Birch, J. W. and Stuckless, E. R.: *The Relationship Between Early Manual Communication and Later Achievement of the Deaf.* U. S. Office of Education Cooperative Research Project No. 1769, Washington, D. C., 1964.

27. Craig, H. B.: A sociometric investigation of the self-concept of the deaf child. *Amer. Ann. Deaf, 110:* 456, 1965.

28. Falberg, R. M.: Acceptance, rejection and over protection. *The Wisconsin Times,* Delavan, Wisc., November 1967.

29. Furth, H. G.: *Thinking Without Language: Psychological Implications of Deafness.* The Free Press, New York, 1966.

30. Kenny, V.: A better way to teach deaf children. *Harpers Magazine,* March 1962.

31. Kohl, H. R.: *Language and Education of the Deaf.* Center for Urban Education, New York, 1966.

32. Little, J. A.: An open letter to parents. *The Minnesota Companion, 93:* 1, November 1967.

33. Meadow, K. P.: *The Effect of Early Manual Communication and Family Climate on the Deaf Child's Development.* Unpublished doctoral dissertation, University of California, 1967.

34. Rainer, J. D. and Altshuler, K. Z.: *Comprehensive Mental Health Services for the Deaf.* New York State Psychiatric Institute, New York, 1966.

35. Rhodes, M. J.: From a parent's point of view, *The Deaf American, 19:* 20, 1967.

36. Stafford, C.: Fingerspelling in the oral classroom, *Amer. Ann. Deaf, 110:* 483, 1965.

37. Stevenson, E. A.: *The California News.* California School for the Deaf, November 19, 1964.

38. Switzer. M. E. and Williams, B. R.: Life problems of deaf people: prevention and treatment. *Arch. Environ. Health, 15:* 249, 1967.

39. Vernon, M.: A guide for the psychological evaluation of deaf and severely hard of hearing adults, *The Deaf American, 19:* 15, 1967.

Psychiatry, Religion and the Deaf

VERY REVEREND JOHN P. HOURIHAN

PSYCHIATRY is one of the newest branches of modern medicine; religion is centuries old. In the development of psychiatry, Freud left the mark of his genius as a man of science; in his *The Future of an Illusion,* he threw a block in the path of mutual assistance that each could give to the other. According to Calvin Hall, the pessimistic viewpoint of this work represents an underlying mood of many of Freud's writings.[1] As a pioneer thinker his lectures and writings on psychiatry and its related fields had great influence. Consequently, converts were won to his philosophical views. Religious people reacted differently and condemned psychiatry as irreligious. Some clergymen even charged that the new science was attempting to become a substitute for religion.

But times are changing as men in both fields become more enlightened and, so, less threatened. Today we are witnessing a rapprochement between psychiatry and religion. The old stereotyped and antithetical images that were called up by the terms *religion* and *psychiatry* are fading. Realizing the values to be gained by such a rapprochement, authorities in both areas have written copiously in the past decade, pointing out the misconceptions and ignorance that are the bases for these erroneous stereotypes.[2, 3, 4, 5] Activities such as the Kokomo Project[6] are bringing the clergy and psychiatrists together for their common interest—man and his spiritual well-being.

Psychiatry and religion have man as their common object of study. Both have a role to play in his mental health and emotional life, but in different ways and for different reasons. What the precise boundaries of these roles are when they impinge upon each other will be the subject of discussions for years to come. At least the discussions have begun.[7] The word *religion* has many meanings. One author, over fifty years ago, listed forty-eight definitions.[5] Some of these connotations are so entirely different that a paper on Psychiatry and Religion demands a brief discussion about the terms themselves.

95

Different men use the term *religion* to reflect their own concepts of religion and its origin. Such concepts may be theistic or nontheistic. Those that are theistic may be polytheistic or monotheistic. The nontheistic expresses belief in some leader whose dictates its adherents follow with some sort of fanaticism. This may be of a political or ideological type and can be aptly called humanistic. As used by Eric Fromm in its broadest meaning, humanistic religion becomes the deification of all men, and the term *God* becomes a symbol of man's powers.[5] Theistic religion posits a faith in a transcendental Power or Powers. It is a natural religion when the knowledge of the divine is achieved by reason alone. It is a revealed religion when truths which are beyond man's ability to arrive at by reason alone are revealed to him. For most theists religion is not born of fear or the need for security. Nor is it the projection of the father-image or a common denominator of the religions of the world. For most theists religion is a real relationship that exists between man and God, a relationship based on a set of truths that lead to the formulation of rules regulating the relationship, rules that are embodied in ceremonials or rites.

Religion that claims to be interested in the bond that exists between man and his Maker should be interested in all men, and especially in those who deviate from what society calls normal or typical. The Mosaic Law and the New Testament give proof of this, and historical accounts of the development of programs for the deaf verify their expectations.[8-12] The compassion of those early times, reflecting the limited knowledge extant, evolved into an increasing respect for the abilities of the deaf as social attitudes changed. The change resulted from the work of pioneering spirits, many of whom worked from religious motives. Although the literature says nothing of their interest in the mental health of their subjects, it is safe to say that, being interested in their intellectual and spiritual development, the early workers must have been concerned about the emotional development of the deaf as well. It is difficult to conceive of educators so wrapped up in their immediate goals that they would overlook such an important aspect of a man's life.

Clergymen were gradually replaced by professional educators of the deaf and, as public education became more prominent, the strong religious atmosphere of deaf schools in America during the first half of the nineteenth century began to change. Less stress was placed on religious training and more on academic and vocational training.[13] Most of the clergy today work outside the official educational framework. In this capacity their role as men of God working for the spiritual good of the deaf is that of a pastor of souls. In this capacity their work as spiritual counselors is heightened, and bears on areas that can bring them directly into contact with psychiatrists and psychologists who are interested in the mental health and emotional life of their people. One study reported that 42 percent of the people who sought psychiatric help went first to their clergy.[14] Another developed six strong reasons which could explain why so many people go to their clergy rather than to the family doctor, or to psychiatrists and psychologists or to social agencies.[6] The percentage might be even greater among the deaf because of the problem of communication.

The problems that come to a clergyman working with the deaf are the same as those coming to the one who works with hearing people—schizophrenia, depression, suicide, anxiety states, phobic states, obsessive-compulsives, paranoid personalities, and those with sexual problems. A scientific approach to the incidence of the types of problems and their correlation with deafness is the work of professionals.[6, 13] The clergyman is more concerned with where he can obtain help for the person.

More and more clergymen are beginning to recognize their limitations in handling certain aspects of these problems. A sophistication that was lacking in this area in the early part of this century is now being developed in the clergy during their training period. In the past 30 years many seminaries have instituted programs to help the clergy distinguish the spiritual from the psychiatric difficulty, and the programs instruct the clergyman about his limitations and the patient's needs in the latter case. As clergymen working with the deaf become more numerous and more knowledgeable about emotional problems, they discover, ironically, that there are few professionals and even less facilities competent to deal with such problems in the deaf population.

It is our fervent prayer that out of this conference will come a thrust that will advance mental health programs for the deaf across the nation.

REFERENCES

1. Hall, C.: *A Primer of Freudian Psychology.* New American Library, New York, 1954.

2. Braceland, F.: *Faith, Reason and Modern Psychiatry.* Kennedy and Sons, New York, 1955.

3. Gassert, R. and Hall, B.: *Psychiatry and Religious Faith.* Viking Press, New York, 1964.

4. Moore, T. V.: *Heroic Sanctity and Insanity.* Grune and Stratton, New York, 1959.

5. Vander Velt, J. and Odenwald, R.: *Psychiatry and Catholicism.* Mc-Graw-Hill, New York, 1952.

6. Westberg, G. and Draper, E.: *Community Psychiatry and the Clergyman.* Charles C. Thomas, Springfield, Ill., 1966.

7. Dominian, J.: *Psychiatry and the Christian.* Hawthorne, New York, 1962.

8. Babbidge, H.: *Education of the Deaf.* U. S. Department of Health, Education, and Welfare, Washington, D. C., 1965.

9. Davis H. and Silverman, S. R.: *Hearing and Deafness.* Holt, Rinehart and Winston, New York, 1960.

10. Goetzinger, C. P.: Psychology of deafness. In *West Coast Regional Institute on Personal, Social and Vocational Adjustment to Total Deafness,* (I. S. Fusfeld, ed.), U. S. Office of Vocational Rehabilitation, Washington, D. C., 1959.

11. Rainer, J. D., Altshuler, K. Z., Kallmann, F. J. and Deming, W. E. (eds.): *Family and Mental Health Problems in a Deaf Population.* New York State Psychiatric Institute, New York, 1963.

12. Stone, M. and Youngs, J.: Catholic education of the deaf in the United States, *Amer. Ann. Deaf, 99:* 411, 1948.

13. Jones, J. W.: One hundred years in the history of the education of the deaf in America and its present status, *Proceedings of the 21st Meeting of the Convention of American Instructors of the Deaf, 21:* 181, 1917.

14. Ziskind, R., Droisen, T. and Plutver, A. I. (eds.): *Viewpoint on Mental Health.* New York City Community Mental Health Board, New York, 1967.

The Relevance of Audiologic Data in Planning Mental Health Services for the Acoustically Impaired

RICHARD F. KRUG

CERTAIN ATTITUDES and understandings appear to be more important than others in developing a sense of well-being, and in determining the status of a person's mental health. It is essential, therefore, that these attitudes should first be identified. Then workers with the deaf should see if audiologic data may play a role in developing or altering understandings, and in changing attitudes. If audiologic data *can* lead to a better understanding of oneself, and therefore alter one's attitudes towards oneself, then such data are relevant to planning mental health services for the acoustically impaired.

In an effort to provide a frame of reference and to relate certain concepts it will be necessary, first, to define terms. The definitions need not be universally accepted, but for purposes of showing relationships among concepts, it is essential that the meaning of the terms used in this discussion be understood.

First let us define the population of acoustically impaired individuals with whom we are concerned, for there is often a misinterpretation of the terms *deaf*, *deafened* and *hard of hearing*. For our purposes, the term *acoustically impaired* refers to all individuals whose hearing sensitivity is not within normal limits. The word *deaf* refers to those who suffer with a loss of hearing incurred so early in life and of such great magnitude that it prevents the learning of language and oral communication through audition.

When the word *deafened* is used, it refers to those individuals who at one time possessed enough hearing to learn language and oral communication through hearing, but who now suffer with a loss of hearing so severe that audition is useless for purposes of receiving oral communication.

The term *hard of hearing* refers to those who possess a hearing loss, but in whom language acquisition through audition has not been precluded. Thus, we will be concerned with individuals who, because of the nature, degree, and onset of the loss of hearing, have failed to develop oral communication skills through audition, as well as with those fortunate enough to have developed language skills through normal channels prior to the loss of all usable hearing. In addition, our concern is with those who retain enough residual hearing to enable them to utilize audition in oral communication.

Audiologists have a difficult time when they try to define the field of audiology and describe its scope of activity. My own brief definition of audiology is *the science of hearing*. It concerns itself with those physical aspects which contribute to the sensation or experience that we call hearing. It is concerned with the individual who exhibits an abnormality of the sensation of hearing and with the habilitative and rehabilitative aspects of such abnormality, exclusive of medical diagnosis and treatment. It is concerned with research, theoretical and applied, directed towards a better understanding of the hearing process, with the physical factors affecting hearing, and with the management of persons exhibiting hearing impairment.

Inasmuch as the field of audiology encompasses diverse activities, it is obvious that no individual audiologist is equally adept in all areas. Indeed, most of them specialize in one or two specific areas. It is therefore important, when seeking the aid of an audiologist, to select one who has an interest and the experience in the area of one's chief concern.

It is considerably more difficult to define the term mental health. In the simplest, most descriptive language, as I will use it, the term *mental health* will be related to the degree to which an individual feels himself adequate in dealing with the physical and social environments. If the individual feels himself to be adequate in meeting and dealing with the everyday problems of life, he develops a sense of well-being, and we might, then, consider him to be in sound mental health. If, on the other hand, the individual feels himself incompetent and inadequate in dealing with the everyday problems of life, then he may be thought of as being in poor mental health. While this may not be an acceptable definition to all, it can nevertheless serve as a basis for this discussion.

Since I cannot pretend to be a psychologist, a psychiatrist, or a mental hygienist, I have leaned heavily upon the work of Carroll[1] who discusses in simple terms those personal understandings and attitudes about oneself which determine one's state of mental health. Each of these determinative factors will be identified, and an attempt will be made to relate each to the acoustically impaired population.

According to Carroll, one important factor leading to sound mental health is to maintain *an attitude of respect for self and a respect for others*. In general, an individual who has respect for himself and respect for other human beings usually enjoys sound mental health. Each of us may, from time to time, find it difficult to maintain self-respect. But consider the additional task of trying to develop such respect when you are singled out as a member of that population which was considered by Aristotle as incapable of learning, and by some ancient groups as unfit to live. How difficult, perhaps, to respect your fellow man, when history reports that he has driven individuals such as yourself from the confines of their home community into the countryside and wilderness because of their deafness.

How difficult it must be to engender respect for your fellow man even today, when portions of society still attempt to pass laws to prevent you from driving a car because you can't hear. And it is far from easy to respect society, when insurance companies and employers view members of your group as bad risks, of which they wish to have no part.

How great a struggle it must be for the deaf or deafened individual to raise his head above the murk and mire of witchery, gross misconception, and sheer nonsense into which he is forced by the majority of society. What tremendous insight it must take to develop a true liking for yourself, when those who share the same label as you, are degraded by society to a position of second-rate citizenship!

While audiologic data can do little or nothing to alter the manner in which society views the acoustically impaired, the sensitive audiologist can work as a professional as well as an individual to improve the attitudes of society toward the acoustically handicapped, and to help the handicapped to respect themselves.

If we are to plan mental health services for the acoustically handicapped, we must seek ways of coordinating the efforts of the many professional fields to the end that the acoustically impaired individual may find it easier to develop a true liking and appreciation of himself, and that society may find it possible to consider him an equal life-sharing partner of this universe.

A second aspect related to sound mental health is *to have an understanding and tolerance of one's limitations and of the limitations of others*. In Carroll's words, a "cardinal principle of mental hygiene is that the realities of life must be seen clearly and, to a considerable extent, accepted."[1] This means adjusting to the conditions of the external world as well as accepting ourselves as we are. If we continue to wage an unrelenting struggle against the realities of the world, we are, indeed, inviting a mental breakdown.

Perhaps it is not too much to say that many of us provide obstacles rather than a helping hand when it comes to aiding the deaf face the realities of life. For how can a deaf individual readily gain insight into the realities of life and his own limitation, when many of the professionals with whom he comes in contact fail to see such realities? I suggest that audiologists, educators of the deaf, administrators of educational programs, and other professionals should attempt with real vigor to seek to separate the realities from the fantasies, the achievable from the methodological, the fact from opinion and prejudice when it comes to establishing educational, vocational, and training programs for the deaf child. It is difficult for me to believe that a deaf child can emerge unscathed from an educational system which philosophically insists that the acoustically impaired child react, behave, believe, and attempt to communicate, exactly as do the fully hearing members of society. The problem can best be crystallized by asking a simple question. How can any deaf or deafened individual stand up to the struggle of pretending to be a hearing individual, when actually he lives in a silent world?

It is in the area of understanding certain human limitations that audiologic data are most relevant. Varying degrees of hearing loss place various limitations upon the ability to respond to sounds of the environment and to receive speech. In general, the greater the degree of hearing loss, the less will be the ability to respond to sound. Therefore, in order to plan an intelligent and realistic mental health program for an acoustically impaired individual, a reliable estimate of residual hearing is essential.

Reliable audiologic information, together with the array of other data and information gathered and assessed by professionals concerned with the mental hygiene of the acoustically impaired, is ultimately destined for two major groups. One is composed of acoustically impaired individuals themselves, and the other primarily of parents who have young deaf children or children with impaired hearing.

It is no secret that states of confusion, bewilderment, and anxiety beset parents when they realize for the first time that their child is deaf, and that there is no hope of restoring hearing. Neither is it a secret that the mental health of the young deaf child will develop to a large degree in keeping with the mental attitudes, goals, aspirations, perceptions, and rational judgments of the parents as they are reflected in the management of the child within the home.

Obviously then, mental health services for the young deaf child begin with a program designed to provide accurate and appropriate information for parents and possibly training for them as well. If the mental hygienist, counselor, and parent are to understand the limitations hearing loss places upon oral communication, the measurement of sensitivity to sound must be a reliable one, and the interpretation of the data must be correct. The interpretation must be concerned not only with the limitations that the loss imposes upon communication skills and the ramifications and implications of this loss for education, but must also emphasize the capabilities of the individual to respond to sound as determined by the degree of residual hearing.

The following example, illustrating the value of audiologic data in planning for a child is undoubtedly not new to personnel of most speech and hearing clinics. A 5-year-old child diagnosed as mentally retarded by one professional person and as emotionally disturbed by a second, appeared for a speech and hearing evaluation. The audiologic evaluation revealed that the child had a high-frequency hearing loss, in which sensitivity to low-frequency sounds was within normal limits, but sensitivity to frequencies above 750 cps was entirely absent. For all practical purposes, this meant that the child was capable of hearing the low-frequency components of speech. Unfortunately, however, she could not hear those frequencies which make speech intelligible or understandable. She was, for instance, aware the psychologist was talking to her, but as she did not understand him, she was unable to respond to his requests or suggestions in a meaningful manner. She could hear her parents talking, but through audition alone could not make out what they had said. Lipreading, coupled with her residual hearing, provided spasmodic periods of accurate communication, and her own speech reflected the distorted speech patterns that she heard.

What was thought to be behavior associated with an emotional problem was actually quite logical behavior for a young child with a high-frequency hearing loss. Again, what was thought to be poor performance on a verbal test of intelligence was logical behavior for a child who failed to understand instructions. While it was foolhardy to assume that there was no emotional overlay associated with the hearing loss, both behavior and communication skills did improve when the parents began treating the child as one who possessed impaired hearing, rather than as one whose primary problem was mental retardation or a serious emotional problem. In this instance, the mental health of the parents no less than that of the child was aided by the inclusion of audiologic data.

A third aspect related to sound mental health is *for each of us to know that behavior is caused.* In general, it is the well-adjusted person who acts without dwelling unduly on the causes of his behavior. However, when he perceives that he is becoming emotionally maladjusted, it is wise for him to ask why. One of the first steps in reducing tension is to discover what is causing it, and to ignore the condition or to pretend that it does not exist, will only tend to intensify and prolong the period of maladjustment.

The behavior of the acoustically impaired individual, like that of the hearing, is determined by the state of the total organism at that particular moment. What may appear to one individual to be intelligent, logical or appropriate behavior in a specific situation may be viewed as stupid, illogical, and inappropriate by another who sees the same behavior. What may be appropriate behavior from the point of view of the acoustically impaired individual, may be interpreted as inappropriate from the point of view of the normal hearing observer. That certain behavior of the acoustically handicapped should differ from that of the hearing is to be expected. Indeed, we should even ask "How *can* an individual with a hearing loss be expected to view his behavior from the same frame of reference as do his hearing peers, when information necessary for such judgments is fragmentary and distorted as compared to that available to hearing individuals?"

Audiologic data can often be of help in describing the logical basis for certain behavioral characteristics. These characteristics may be those observed in the individual possessing the hearing loss, or they may be those observed in the hearing population by the deaf or deafened individual. One example may illustrate the point. A junior high school girl was referred to a university speech and hearing clinic by a public school therapist for additional help in improving speech. The girl, although not deaf, had a loss of hearing of the degree and configuration that made it difficult for her to understand the speech of others unless she was both looking at and intently listening to the speaker. Her own speech was somewhat difficult to understand at times, and appeared to reflect the distorted speech patterns that she heard. She was disturbed with her classmates and friends on two accounts. First, when her classmates asked her to repeat what she had said, she felt that they were teasing her and deliberately poking fun at her. In her own words she said to the clinician, "I speak just like they do, and I don't see why they ask me to say it over . . . or why they say, huh." She was serious—and upset, for she honestly felt that her speech was of the same quality as that of her classmates. Also, she failed to realize that the behavior exhibited by her classmates was, in part, a reaction to her own poor speech. In addition, she felt that they did not speak loud enough or clearly enough. In her words, "Some of them don't know how to talk." She had received speech therapy for a number of years in the public school, and wanted no part of additional emphasis on improving it. While this young girl could verbalize the fact that she had a hearing loss, she appeared either unaware or afraid of what it meant in terms of impaired communication. Although she was initially referred for additional speech therapy, the major goal of clinical therapy was to help her understand the ramifications of her hearing loss, to relate the hearing loss to the reception of speech, and to relate her own speech patterns to her hearing loss. Attempts were made to help her interpret her own reactions and the reactions of others in relation to imperfect communication or distorted information. Now she finds it possible to accept more realistically the limitations imposed upon her by her hearing loss, and is working on improving her speech, auditory discrimination, spelling, and speechreading skills.

It is necessary to emphasize the fact that the degree and configuration of the hearing loss are only two factors to consider, and that it is erroneous to believe that *all* behavior of the acoustically impaired individual is determined solely by these factors. It is erroneous also to consider that all of oral communicative behavior is determined solely by the *sensitivity* to sound. On the other hand, to ignore exploring the relationship between hearing loss and observed behavioral traits is to overlook a factor that for some individuals is a potent determinant of social behavior.

In addition to, (1) a respect for self and others, (2) an understanding of the limitations of oneself and others, and (3) an appreciation of the fact that behavior is caused, sound mental health is achieved when the individual understands and satisfies the fundamental needs he shares with all human beings. These needs can be grouped into three major categories: (1) the need for physical security, (2) the need for emotional security, and (3) the need for achievement and status. If all of these needs are met to the satisfaction of the individual, they contribute to a feeling of well-being which is analogous to sound mental health.

Physical security, is obtained, in part, by satisfying the basic biologic needs of the individual. It may be difficult to achieve when one is suffering from air hunger, sleep hunger, food hunger, or sex hunger. Physical security is also enhanced when one is free of pain and of immediate danger. These factors are significant. But the deaf and deafened have got to deal with an additional factor not shared by the hearing, for they cannot monitor the environment auditorily and perceive changes in it, as do the hearing. Myklebust[2] considers hearing as one of the distant senses, characterized as maintaining an all-directional, uninterrupted, or continuous contact with the environment. Generally, hearing is the primary sense that is used to scan the background environment, while vision and other senses attend to the foreground. (Under certain circumstances, hearing can serve foreground needs, while vision can also serve background needs.)

To deny an individual the possibility of continuous scanning of the environment by audition is to deny him the opportunity to note the immediate changes in activity denoted by sound. To check the environment, therefore, the deaf and deafened must rely on vision as a means of monitoring background as well as foreground activity. Since vision is not all-directional and can be interrupted by factors such as the amount of available light, the position of the head, obstacles in the line of vision, and sleep, the probability that a deaf or deafened person can be surprised or frightened by unanticipated changes in the environment is increased.

Again, audiologic data relative to degree and configuration of hearing loss may be pertinent in planning a program of mental hygiene for certain individuals. Such data may be used to help parents of young deaf children understand the observed behavior of their child, and such information may be of value in counseling with the adult or young adult who is finding it difficult to feel secure in his day-to-day encounters with his environment.[3, 4]

Emotional security is a second need to be met before a feeling of well-being can be established. There is no doubt that every need or motive has an emotional concomitant. The emotional aspect can be an aid in organizing the pieces of the mosaic of experience, or it can become a factor in disrupting a state of relative satisfaction. Human beings tend to seek satisfaction of their needs in a way which brings to them acceptance and understanding rather than criticism and rejection. It is unusual, indeed, for an individual who is subjected to sharp criticism over an extended period of time to maintain his emotional balance.

Consider then, the plight of the congenitally deaf person who, because of the inability to communicate freely and easily with the hearing population is most often turned aside, avoided, or rejected in one way or another. Is it, then, any wonder that the deaf as a group, and particularly the youth and adults, seek the company of other deaf individuals rather than seeking social satisfaction with the hearing?[4] Perhaps it is the social circle of *deaf* friends which provides much of the emotional security for the individual and prevents mental problems among the deaf from being greater in number than they are now.

Individual achievement and some degree of status are a third need each human being seeks to fulfill. Each person must master or control those aspects of the environment which are important to him. To attempt to do so without effective oral communication, to strive to attain success in competition with hearing society, to reach for high education goals, to advance vocationally when communication skills and certain social poise are lacking is difficult, and the problem encountered may tend to negate attempts of the deaf to move ahead and to achieve in activities of their own choosing.

What is the probability of a deaf individual satisfying his need for personal achievement when the levels of performance among the deaf are generally below those of the hearing population? What are the prospects of a deaf individual attaining his level of aspiration, when he aspires to levels identical with those of the hearing population? What is the prospect of obtaining the approval of society for what is done, when the yardstick of success of the deaf is the same as that applied to the hearing?

Although audiologic data cannot predict the level of academic or vocational achievement nor the social poise and competence that an individual may develop, such data can be used in planning educational programs for acoustically impaired children and in vocational planning for adults. Since status is intricately related to educational and vocational achievement levels, and since each of these is related to the state of mental health, professionals dealing with mental health services for the deaf simply cannot ignore audiologic data.

Audiologic data provide information regarding the ability of the individual to respond to sound, yet they in no way predict what use will be made by that individual of the sound available. Perhaps, it is the state of mental health that dictates what use is made of sound that is available or how much an individual gains from his educational, vocational, and social training.

Audiologic data, then, are relevant to the planning of mental health services for the acoustically impaired. It is therefore necessary to provide some basic information relating the degree of hearing loss to the reception of sound, to the degree of disruption in oral communication, and to the generally accepted types of educational planning needed. The accompanying figure (Figure 1) is such an attempt. Of course, the generalities do not hold true for every acoustically impaired individual, but they can serve as guidelines by which to anticipate communication behavior and predict the degree of difficulty in using audition for the gathering of information.

REFERENCES

1. Carroll, H. A.: *Mental Hygiene, the Dynamics of Adjustment.* Prentice-Hall, New Jersey, 1964.
2. Myklebust, H. R.: *Psychology of Deafness.* Grune and Stratton, New York, 1960.
3. Myklebust, H. R.: Psychological and psychiatric implications of deafness. *Arch. Otolaryngology, 78:* 790, 1963.
4. Rainer, J. D., Altshuler, K. Z., Kallmann, F. J., and Deming, W. E. (eds.): *Family and Mental Health Problems in a Deaf Population.* New York State Psychiatric Institute, New York, 1963.

Figure 1: Hearing Loss and the Ability to Hear Normal Conversation, the Development of Speech and Language, and the Educational Management Required

Category or Description	Range of Pure Tone Loss, Average 1951 ASA	Range of Pure Tone Loss, Average 1964 ISO	Effect of Hearing Loss on Reception of Speech and Environmental Sounds	Effect of Hearing Loss on Development of Speech and Language	Educational Management
Normal	less than 20 dB	less than 30 dB	No adverse effect	No adverse effect	No special educational procedures.
Mild loss (Hard of hearing)	20 dB—30 dB	30 dB—40 dB	Difficulty in hearing faint speech at a distance. May experience no appreciable communication breakdown in school if preferential seating arranged.	If defective speech observed, causative factor probably not hearing loss. Will be able to learn speech normally by audition.	Preferential seating in regular classroom.
Marginal loss (Hard of hearing)	30 dB—40 dB	40 dB—50 dB	Hears average conversational speech at a distance of 3 feet, but will have trouble in a group. Can carry on face-to-face conservation but difficulty increases as distance from speaker increases. May miss as much as 50% of class discussion if voices are faint or speaker not in his line of vision.	May exhibit slight distortion or substitution of speech sounds. May have slightly limited vocabulary.	Speech reading. Individual hearing aid, if prescribed and training in its use. (Hearing aid orientation) Auditory training. Preferential seating in classroom. Speech therapy if necessary. Attention to vocabulary development if necessary.
Moderate loss (Hard of hearing)	40 dB—60 dB	50 dB—70 dB	Can understand loud conversational speech at a distance of about 3 feet. Will have increas-	Greater number of distortions and some omissions of speech sounds.	Speech reading. Speech training. Preferential seating.

			...tions requiring participation in group discussions. Social intercourse is clearly affected. Background and foreground use of audition is essentially precluded, therefore, responds to foreground.	...ment. Evidence of limited vocabulary. May learn speech and language through hearing when sound is amplified.	...special class placement, if necessary.
Severe loss (Deaf, educationally deaf or partially deaf)	60 dB—80 dB	70 dB—90 dB	Can hear only amplified speech. May be able to hear moderately-loud voice at several inches from the ear. Will hear loud noises at some distance, auto horns, dogs barking, etc. Can identify environmental noises and may distinguish vowels but have difficulty with consonants. Relies on other sensory systems for monitoring the environment.	Speech and language do not develop spontaneously. Voice quality may show signs of deviation. Need to learn to communicate through use of special techniques. Personal-social and general environmental contact is difficult.	Speech reading. Speech education for the deaf. Emphasis on speech, language development. Preferential seating. Hearing aid and auditory training.
Profound loss (Deaf)	80 dB+	90 dB+	Unaware of loud noises but may respond reflexively to loud sounds close to the ear. Sound has no meaning. Cannot understand amplified sound.	Speech and language do not develop spontaneously. Voice quality and intonation deviate greatly.	Speech reading. Special education for the deaf. Hearing aid and auditory training.

The Government's Role in Funding
Mental Health Services for the Deaf

JOSEPH ROSENSTEIN

IN THE PAST few years, the government has re-emphasized its commitment to handicapped children and adults by the extension and expansion of educational and rehabilitative services. Federal legislation, during the past decade, clearly reveals that the government intends the handicapped to be not only recognized, but assured an education in order to take their place in and to contribute to our society. Many persons have spearheaded these recent efforts. We can identify the leadership of President Lyndon B. Johnson, the late President John F. Kennedy, Senators Lester Hill of Alabama and Wayne Morse of Oregon, Congressman Hugh L. Carey of New York, and the late Congressman John Fogarty of Rhode Island—to name but a few who have dedicated their energies to the cause of providing increased services to all the handicapped. The net result of their efforts enables us to implement and initiate more programs to serve the handicapped.

Within the Department of Health, Education, and Welfare, there are several offices and divisions that afford possibilities for the funding of services for the deaf, as well as for deaf persons with emotional problems.

Social and Rehabilitation Service

Boyce Williams of the Rehabilitation Services Administration (RSA) of Social and Rehabilitation Service (SRS), during his years of government service, has helped initiate several programs currently in existence that focus on the mental health of the deaf. Let me mention some of the current projects funded by SRS and their activities.

The Research and Training Center in Deafness at New York University, in addition to its responsibility for the preparation of rehabilitation workers and research, in 1967 held a short-term training course in deafness for psychiatrists, in conjunction with the New York Psychiatric

111

Institute staff. Later this spring, (1968) a repeat of the course will be held at New York University, with a view to spreading understanding of the need, and further to explore ways of attacking the problem. DePaul University has established a long-term training program that offers in-depth study of the problems of deafness and communication skills for psychiatrists. Planning for a community mental health program has been initiated by the California Department of Mental Hygiene at the Langley Porter Neuropsychiatric Institute in San Francisco. Psychiatric and other services to psychotic deaf persons are being offered and evaluated at the Michael Reese Hospital and Medical Center in Chicago. A personal and family counseling program for the deaf has been undertaken by the Family Services Agency of Los Angeles with a somewhat more preventive approach in mind. Pittsburgh's Counseling and Community Services Center for the Deaf has reached out to stimulate both the interest of and participation by the chief of the psychiatric staff of Dixmont Hospital to provide psychiatric services to the deaf. Although not funded by Rehabilitation Services Administration, community services and counseling programs in Seattle, Kansas City (Missouri), Wichita, and Dallas have been instituted as a result of consultative assistance of RSA staff members. And, of course, there is the commendable continuing work of the New York State Psychiatric Institute, which is adding to its former achievements the establishment of a halfway house and day-care center for deaf discharged psychiatric patients, as well as undertaking the responsibility for convening this present workshop.

The above-mentioned projects, programs, workshops, and service centers all came into existence through funds made available to RSA by the Vocational Rehabilitation Act, as amended, through 1965, and the Vocational Rehabilitation Amendments of 1967 (P.L. 90-99). This Act authorizes five major programs, under each of which deaf persons with mental health problems would be entitled to receive services.

The Vocational Rehabilitation Services Program provides grants to State vocational rehabilitation agencies to cover part of the cost of services for physically or mentally disabled persons whose disability is a substantial handicap to employment, and who can be reasonably expected to be rehabilitated into gainful employment. These services include diagnosis, comprehensive evaluation, counseling, training and placement, follow up, and assistance payments (75 percent of costs) for medical and related services. Assistance in establishing rehabilitation facilities is also available, including expansion, remodeling, or alterations of existing buildings, and for acquiring initial equipment and for initial staffing (the first year). Nonprofit agencies should contact their State vocational rehabilitation agencies for information on funding possibilities.

The second program, entitled *Vocational Rehabilitation Innovation Grants*, also provides to State agencies up to 75 percent of the cost of grants for the innovation of services which are new (or new to the

State), or are designed for groups of handicapped persons having disabilities which are particularly severe. Programs funded for juvenile offenders, for example, are: (1) the assignment of a vocational rehabilitation counselor to a county court, to evaluate cases referred to a diagnostic and probation center; and (2) the establishment of a coordinated program of counselor aid services throughout a State, to assist the youthful offender in making the transition from correctional institutions into employment and community living. It would seem that this program holds promise for the funding of innovative mental health projects and services for the deaf.

State vocational rehabilitation agencies also receive funds, some of which can be distributed to public and other nonprofit agencies, for planning, preparing, and initiating special programs concerned with the expansion of existing vocational rehabilitation services. Construction grants for the building, planning, and staffing of rehabilitation facilities and workshops are made available, through the State agency, to nonprofit agencies, institutions, or organizations in the third vocational rehabilitation program administered by the Division of Disability Services, RSA, SRS, entitled the *Facilities and Workshop Program.*

The Training Grant Program administered through the Division of Training of RSA makes grants available to State agencies, public and other nonprofit agencies and organizations, and educational institutions for part of the cost of training. Grants for short-term training can be obtained by profit-making organizations, as well as those just mentioned, and can cover the total cost of the training course. Grants are being made under this program for support of specialized training for rehabilitation of the deaf and the mentally ill, among others, and for curricula of interdisciplinary training. Forms for short-term training are available from the Chief of the Division of Training, RSA, SRS, and are accepted at any time during the year. Regional office staff are available for assistance in the preparation of applications. Long-term training grants have an annual deadline of May 1st for September funding.

The Vocational Rehabilitation Research and Demonstration Grant Program, administered by the Division of Research and Demonstration of RSA, provides grants for partial support of research and demonstration projects. Matching ratios of Federal and grantee support are a matter of administrative determination. Private profit-making agencies and individuals are not eligible. Inquiries for general information and for obtaining application forms and deadlines should be addressed to the Chief of the Division.

Additional sources of funding from SRS include the crippled children's and the maternal and child health programs, administered by the Division of Health Service, Children's Bureau (SRS). Moneys for services for handicapped persons, including the deaf, are granted to State crippled children's agencies for services to individual clients. Under the provisions of the Social Security Amendments of 1967, there is nothing that would disallow psychiatric services to deaf children with additional handicaps. Currently, however, the Children's Bureau is not funding any trainees or projects dealing directly with the mental health of the deaf. The Maternal and Child Health Branch sponsors 15 regional diagnostic clinics, specifically concerned with services to the multiply-handicapped child, which conceivably could involve the emotionally-disturbed deaf child, if appropriate personnel were available. While most of the grants must be applied for through the State agencies, some funding for research and demonstration is done through the Federal Office.

The Division of Mental Retardation, formerly within the Public Health Service (PHS) is also now a part of SRS. Under the authority of P.L. 88-164, the Mental Retardation Facilities and Community Mental Health Centers Construction Act, and especially the Mental Retardation Amendments of 1967 (P.L. 90-170), grants are provided for the construction of university-affiliated facilities that will include programs for persons with other neurological handicapping conditions that are found to be significantly associated with mental retardation. There are currently 14 university-affiliated facilities dealing primarily with the mentally retarded. Under the new provisions of the amendments, it would be reasonable to expect that multiply-handicapped deaf persons will be able to benefit from these existing programs. Federal funds under this program may be used to pay up to three-fourths of the costs of construction of facilities that provide a full range of inpatient and outpatient services for the mentally retarded.

Public Health Service

The Community Mental Health Centers Program is administered by the National Institute of Mental Health (NIMH), of the United States Public Health Service. To date this program has aided over 300 communities, contributing a portion of the costs of construction or remodeling, and of initial staffing of such centers. To qualify, a center must offer at least these five services: inpatient and outpatient treatment, partial hospitalization, emergency services, and consultation and education. Applications from private or nonprofit organizations and from State or other public agencies must be submitted through and approved by the State mental health authority or the State Hill-Burton agency.

Hill-Burton construction funds for hospital and medical facilities (under the Public Health Service Act, Title VI) are also available as grants and loans for assistance in building and equipping hospital and medical facilities. Applications, available through the State health department of the Division of Hospital and Medical Facilities of the PHS, must be approved by the State Health agency, the Public Health Service, and, in the case of rehabilitation facilities, the Rehabilitation Services Administration.

The National Institute of Mental Health (NIMH) has the additional authority for administering research projects, both individual and programmatic. Although the Division of Extramural Research Programs has not as yet awarded grants for research dealing with aspects of emotional disturbances associated with deafness, the agency is willing to consider proposals in this area, provided they meet the standards of reviewing advisory panels. Deadlines are set every four months beginning February 1; matching funds are not required; and individuals, as well as agencies and institutions, may apply for research grants, which, again, are awarded primarily on the basis of the merits of the proposed application.

Colleges and universities and other institutions may apply to the NIMH for training and fellowship grants in the mental health disciplines, including psychiatry, psychology, social work, psychiatric nursing and others. Graduate and postgraduate support is available for the professional training of research workers and practitioners. Support is also available for the continuing education for professionals already in the field and for training some types of supportive personnel. Individuals must apply through the training institution. Stipends for the various professional programs vary. The Division of Manpower and Training Programs of the NIMH will supply application forms, further information, and lists of participating universities and institutions.

The National Institute of Child Health and Human Development (NICHHD), under the same authority that established the aforementioned university-affiliated centers (P.L. 88-164) makes grants available that are designed to: "assist in meeting the cost of construction of facilities for research, or research and related purposes, relating to human development, whether biological, medical, social, or behavioral, which may assist in finding the causes, and means of prevention, of mental retardation, or in finding means of ameliorating the effects of mental retardation." As of about a year ago, 11 such centers had been established, all with heavy interdisciplinary programming. The research program of the NICHHD is a potential source for funding of needed research in human development; under the Growth and Development Program it would be possible, for example, to fund normative research on the personality development of the deaf individual from birth to 21 years of age. Any research which stresses the developmental and normative aspects of deafness might be fundable through this agency, which up to now has provided funds in the somewhat related area of psycholinguistic studies with hearing persons.

The Public Health Service's *National Center for Chronic Disease Control Program* has administrative responsibility for two types of programs through which funds may be available for mental health services for the deaf. The Neurological and Sensory Diseases Control Program awards money for short-term training of psychiatrists, usually at medical schools and centers, and is providing grants for the graduate training of speech pathologists and audiologists. Its authority may also be extended to the training of related professionals, such as EEG technicians. These are training grants to individuals, which become available through the institutions that apply. Although the programs lean toward organic medical involvement, some funds could conceivably be applied to the training of professionals to work with deaf persons with emotional problems.

Moneys for services to patients are available through the Community Services Section of the National Center for Chronic Disease Control Program. This section also includes funds for equipment, renovation, and staffing.

State health and mental health agencies may be eligible for grants for comprehensive public health services under the authority of P.L. 87-749, entitled *Partnership for Health*. These funds are intended to assist states in establishing and maintaining comprehensive services—community, mental, environmental. At least 15 percent of each state's allotment must be allocated to the State mental health authority to provide mental health services. The allotment is made on the basis of per capita income and population. There are also provisions with no matching funds required, for training and for research and demonstrations that are designed to lead to improved or more effective comprehensive mental health planing. Public or non-profit agencies, institutions, or other organizations concerned with health may apply either to the Regional Health Directors of HEW Regional Offices, or to the Office of Comprehensive Health Planning and Development, Office of the Surgeon General, PHS, Bethesda, Maryland 20203.

Services to mentally-ill deaf persons are being provided at St. Elizabeth's Hospital, a federally supported institution in the Washington, D. C. area. Currently, 68 deaf patients are being serviced by audiologists and by volunteers from Gallaudet College, and are receiving religious support from a Gallaudet minister. Psychiatrists there have learned the sign language and conduct psychodrama with eleven deaf patients. Group therapy and recreation sessions, occupational therapy, dance therapy, and art therapy are also available to these patients.

Office of Education

Within the Office of Education, the bulk of Federal moneys that might pertain to emotionally disturbed deaf children is available through the new Bureau of Education for the Handicapped, created to implement P.L. 85-926, as amended. This law provides funds to support research or demonstration programs, and the training of personnel in all areas of work with the handicapped. The Bureau's Division of Educational Services administers additional programs under P.L. 89-313, which amends Titles I and VI of the Elementary and Secondary Act of 1965, and which authorizes grants to states to initiate, expand, and improve educational services to handicapped children. Awards are made to individual state institutions and agencies through the State Education Agency, which must submit its State plan annually. State-operated residential treatment centers for the emotionally disturbed are benefiting from this program, as are private facilities utilized by the state agencies for their handicapped children. Funds may be used for expansion of staff, acquisition of materials and equipment, and relevant research or demonstration projects and programs developing increased and improved services to handicapped children.

Title VI of the Elementary and Secondary Education Act also provides grants to State education agencies, to expand and improve educational and related services for handicapped children in preschool, elementary, and secondary *public* schools.

The program of Captioned Films for the Deaf is administered by the Division of Educational Services within the Bureau of Education for the Handicapped.

The training of teachers and other educational personnel is administered by the Bureau's Division of Training Programs. Last year, 60 college and university training programs for teachers of the emotionally disturbed were supported, and 52 training programs preparing teachers of the deaf received grants. Colleges and universities make yearly applications for undergraduate and graduate traineeships and fellowships, for summer session traineeships, for special study institutes of at least three days' duration, and for grants for the development of new programs. Although training funds are awarded separately in each area of handicap, it is possible to receive funds for the preparation of teachers to work with multiply-handicapped children.

Research and demonstration grants relating to the education of handicapped children are available to state and local education agencies, as well as to public and nonprofit private educational or research organizations and institutions of higher education through the Bureau's Division of Research. Matching funds are required, but in no specific percentage. Proposal forms are available, and are evaluated according to educational significance, soundness of design or operational plan, adequacy of personnel and facilities, and economic efficiency. There are no deadlines set for applications under this program.

Other federal programs support teacher-training projects that include work with emotionally disturbed children. The *Experienced Teacher Fellowship Program,* Higher Education Act of 1965 (P.L. 89-329), encourages experienced teachers to upgrade their teaching skills so as to strengthen elementary and secondary education. It provides graduate fellowships of up to two years for experienced school teachers and for specialists who are recommended by local school systems. Fellowships are allocated in blocs to colleges and universities whose projects for experienced teachers have received approval from the new Bureau of Educational Personnel Development.

Institutes are held for teachers of disadvantaged youth under the National Defense Education Act of 1958, as amended (P.L. 85-926), Title XI. This program provides financial assistance in the form of contracts with institutions of higher education for courses of advanced study for teachers of disadvantaged youths as either short-term institutes or programs for an academic year. This program is administered through the Bureau of Elementary and Secondary Education.

What's Ahead

The most advanced legislative development providing educational services to children is the Education Professional Development Act, (P.L. 90-35), signed by President Johnson in June 1967. It is to be implemented in fiscal year 1969. This legislation, a milepost marking Federal interest in education, is designed to provide funds for the support of projects that identify personnel needs in special and regular education, and to encourage recruitment and training programs for needed personnel.

Under the Education Professional Development Act, financial assistance may be given to State education agencies, local education agencies, institutions of higher education, and public and private agencies, institutions, and organizations in order to attract qualified people into the field of education. Graduate fellowship programs will be available for personnel interested in training, in educational and instructional television, in radio, and in child development.

Short-term training programs will be available from the Bureau of Educational Personnel Development to qualifying programs in a wide range of additional teaching and support specialities. Guidance counselors, social workers, child psychologists, educational media specialists, teacher aids, administrators, craftsmen, artists, and the like may apply. Professionals interested in the emotionally disturbed can now begin to plan programs to train child-care workers for the hundreds of treatment centers throughout the nation. The promise of such training programs for those who work with emotionally-disturbed deaf children is self-evident.

Legislation now receiving consideration by the Congress is also relevant to the future of programs and services with which we are immediately concerned. A new bill (H.R. 12631) has been introduced in the House of Representatives, "to provide temporary authority to expedite procedures for consideration and approval of projects drawing upon more than one Federal assistance program, to simplify requirements for the operations of those projects, and for other purposes." If and when enacted, it will be known as the "Joint Funding Simplification Act." The bill proposes that states, local agencies, and other private and public institutions use Federal assistance more effectively and efficiently to suit particular needs by requesting joint support from more than one Federal agency. Through its provisions, State and Federal resources may be more efficiently combined to support projects of common interest. By providing combined programs of mental health, educational and rehabilitative services for deaf emotionally-disturbed persons, the possibility of joint support will exist to an even greater extent than is now possible.

I have tried to explain how the government has done its job in providing the legislative authority for your needs. To paraphrase a recent statement, let me close by saying: "Don't ask what your country has to offer you; ask how you can make use of what it has to offer."

Discussion Group I: Education

Introduction: The problems of mental health in the deaf are reflections of the poor mental health atmosphere in educational facilities for the deaf and in the homes of the deaf. For a century, this field of special education has been fraught with frustration, conflict, defensiveness, and the like, and the homes of deaf children are too often the unfortunate beneficiaries of this instability. It is understandable, therefore that products of these homes should reflect the level of frustration affecting the total environment of deaf persons.

The field might be compared to the plight of an alcoholic. It is difficult, or impossible to aid the alcoholic until he admits his alcoholism and his need of help. Educators of the deaf are only now beginning to admit to a degree of failure, to face the fact that help is necessary in the complex problems with which they deal. The very fact that we are beginning to look critically at ourselves is itself an indication of improved mental health.

Recent studies show that in most areas educators are not meeting the needs of the deaf, and that regardless of methods or school settings the job of preparation for total living has not been adequately done. Educators are beginning to realize that other disciplines have much to offer them. This meeting, then, is most timely, for educators are ripe for receiving direction, assistance, and some kind of guidelines for mental health programs in the school setting.

The responsibility of educators of the deaf in the area of mental health is awesome; it begins the moment a child is identified as being deaf, and continues to the grave. Universally, mental health is considered a product of early environment. Educators, however, are unfortunately not always the captain of their own ship. They are not always able to carry out that program which they know is best, for conservative tax payers and conservative appropriation committees often control their programs. However, a meeting such as this may arouse the group to the point where previous insurmountable barriers are made to succumb to renewed and revitalized efforts. Educators are aware that they are entrusted with a large part of the burden for better mental health for the deaf; they accept the fact that they are sometimes made the whipping

119

boy by members of other disciplines. But they also accept the willingness of these disciplines to help them with a difficult task.

The education group concluded that while they should strive for perfection, significant improvement can and must be their initial goal.

Mental Health Problems in the School Setting: Descriptions of those mental health problems found in the school setting include: Student withdrawal; poor relation to peers; marked disparity between achievement and potential; aggressive acting-out behavior (such as bullying or being disruptive in class or dormitory); inability to relate positively to authority (teachers, houseparents); stealing; telling wild tales; bizarre thinking or behavior; indication of confused sexual identification, as for example in homosexual acting out; too much conformity or too much passivity; running away or hiding; imaginary illness, frequent visits to infirmary; callousness, difficulty in being reached; poor self-concept; distractibility.

These problems generally come to the school administrator's attention when the child is excluded from groups because of deviant behavior. Such exclusion may occur in the school setting or dormitory, or the teacher or house parent may make the report to the department head. Sometimes other children tell the houseparent of unusual behavior, or the medical staff may report hypochondriacs or those with suspected organic involvements. Parents report, generally after a visit home. There may be recurring reports by the child himself of persecution by peers.

Handling of Mental Health Problems: Some schools have psychologists to provide guidance and counseling service either on their staff, or in a consultation capacity. Minor problems may be counseled by staff-teacher, houseparent or administrative personnel. Severe cases are usually sent home, with advice to parents to get assistance from other resources (that are too often unavailable).

Several schools have clearly defined programs for handling mental health problems. These include:

FLORIDA

The Florida School for the Deaf has a referral committee consisting of the psychologist, the audiologist, the supervising teacher, and the principal. Children with behavior problems are considered by this committee. Teachers and houseparents who are involved appear before the committee to present their observations. After extended discussion relative to the problem of the particular child a recommendation is made. This may be a change of dormitory room, a new direction in the handling of the child, or, if need be, psychiatric assistance. This last requires confirmation by the school physician.

MINNESOTA

A Minnesota law, passed in 1967, states that "any school district may provide instruction and services to handicapped children who have not yet attained school age." (In the state, schooling for hearing-impaired children is mandatory from ages 4-21.) At present, approval of programs is being granted only for hearing-impaired preschoolers. "Preschool" covers the period from birth to age 4, at which time mandatory school district responsibility requires, for educational purposes, either local service or placement of a hearing-impaired child in a day or residential setting.

Implementation of this law consists of regionalization of educational services, and the triangulation of parent, child, and special-education teacher to foster a parent's realistic acceptance of the child's hearing loss and the sharing of responsibility for appropriate child growth and development.

Components of the comprehensive preschool program are: parent counseling and guidance in group and individual therapy sessions; nursery school experience for the deaf child together with hearing children; in-service training of nursery school teachers, and periodic site visitation of nursery schools serving a hearing-impaired child; individual tutoring, as an essential supplement to group activity, by a teacher of the deaf, for beginning linguistic and auditory stimulation.

A Title VI Planning Project ESEA has been funded (February 1968) to train ten parent counselors in and around the state's Twin Cities. Training will be offered as a seminar of eight weekly three-hour meetings to teachers of the deaf and audiologists.

KANSAS

A program under Title I, ESEA, provides a full-time psychologist who is experienced with the deaf, to do evaluations. The psychologist also counsels individual children with mental health problems and counsels with houseparents, teachers, and others who have contact with children with specific difficulties.

All houseparents are required to attend in-service training, under a program jointly funded by school and Title I—ESEA. Class sessions are 1½ hours per week, and are conducted by psychologist, principal, superintendent, supervisory teacher, or invited consultants from such disciplines as medicine or social work. The program includes: Child Development, Child Psychology, Psychology of Deafness, Communication, Group Behavior, Discipline, Leisure-time Activities, and the like.

The School uses its own funds to sponsor two teams from the school—administrative and supervisory—who travel to various locations to hold meetings for parents of deaf children. These teams discuss the school program and the parents' role. They present ideas for developing a better understanding by parents of their deaf child, his needs and his problems.

A "Guide for Parents of Preprimary Deaf Children," has been prepared, including things parents can do with children to foster language development, how to take care of a hearing aid, etc. A Parent Institute has been set up for parents of deaf children not yet enrolled in school to orient them to having a deaf child in the home. Parents of preprimary children are required to come to school for conferences, observations of classes, etc.

Elsewhere, some schools conduct communication classes for parents; others have training programs for houseparents and teachers, while a few schools teach sex hygiene, but this is felt to be a weak area.

Weaknesses in Present Program: To date the educator has been solely responsible not only for the educational management of the hearing-impaired child, but for his emotional and social management as well. It is felt that the educational start for the hearing-impaired child has been too late, in view of the almost total absence of early parent guidance and home training for the pre-school-age child. At the same time, the secondary level has failed to tailor the program to individual needs. With respect to personnel, there is a lack of social workers in consultation with residential institutions. There is also a lack of mental health orientation in general in teacher-training programs, and a wholly inadequate emphasis on this area in teacher-training programs for the education of the deaf. A pleasing personality and emotional stability should be requisites for both teachers and houseparents. In regard to houseparents, the ratio of houseparents to pupils is totally inadequate. There is also a need for ongoing education of non-classroom personnel, to obviate the present sterility of dormitory life.

Another great weakness is what might be termed a *parental vacuum.* Communication should, but does not, involve triangulation of parent, teacher, and child. With communication the key, every available educational method appropriate to the child's individual needs should be utilized. Unfortunately what is found today among students is a lack of feeling of self-worth, self-responsibility, and self-motivation.

It is further felt that the whole community needs to become involved in order for the necessary improvements to be accomplished and that a serious lack of good public relations exists.

Recommendations

The recommendations of the education group fall into the following categories: personnel, parent education, the deaf themselves, government activity, and research.

Personnel: Those working with deaf people often have difficulty in distinguishing between: (1) behavior of the deaf which could be symptomatic of impending or existing emotional disorder, (2) behavior which may be non-conforming or disruptive but yet is frequently observed—or even expected—at a given age in non-handicapped persons; and (3) behavior which can be understood as being the direct result of the handicap of deafness. Therefore, it is recommended that educational material for such workers be prepared in printed form by psychiatrists and psychologists who have had adequate experience with and orientation to the deaf child in his environment. Such material should identify specifically for non-psychiatric workers those behavioral signs which are indicative of emotional disturbance, and which should be the basis for a psychiatric or psychological referral.

Since emotional problems of the deaf frequently have their genesis during the school years, it is recommended that all schools and programs for the deaf include personnel trained in diagnosis and counseling, in order to effect the child's best possible adjustment.

It is further recommended that every educational facility for deaf children should include adequate social work services. Such parent-teacher-child programs and/or services should follow the deaf child throughout his developmental years.

Ongoing, in-service training of houseparents is recommended, for the child spends a great deal of time in a non-academic setting under their direction. Such training should include an understanding of child development and behavior and ways of encouraging in the child a sense of self-worth, personal responsibility, and self-motivation.

It is recommended that funding be made possible through appropriate government agencies (See also under Government Activity) for programs to meet the critical need for these trained supervisory personnel or houseparents in residential schools for the deaf.

It is recommended that there be a consultant on the deaf at the state level (See also under Government Activity) who would assist schools and other agencies in providing mental health services. Preparatory to the setting up of adequate psychiatric services for deaf persons in all parts of our country, it is recommended that the New York State Psychiatric Institute be encouraged to assist other states or agencies to develop such programs through workshops, conferences, and other appropriate activities.

It is recommended that institutions offering a program of teacher preparation in education of the deaf provide a full exposure to deaf adults as well as to deaf children through their practicum courses.

Parent Education (See also under Government Activity): For the deaf two-way communication between parent and child is of the utmost importance. Therefore it is recommended that parents be encouraged to employ whatever medium—oral or manual—to bring about the most facile communication between them and their children. Further, since emotional stability and intellectual growth are dependent upon a healthy parent-child relationship, to which a parent needs to bring mature acceptance of his child's hearing loss and understanding of the impact of deafness upon every facet of the child's growth and development, it is recommended that appropriate parent education and guidance be the ongoing responsibility of the appropriate educational institution or community agency, from the day of diagnosis of hearing loss in a child to adulthood.

Utilization of the Deaf Themselves (See also under Government Activity): It is recommended that programs in the orientation of deaf people as well as of deaf parents to the problems of deafness and all its social ramifications be incorporated in the curricula of schools for the deaf. Captioned Films for the Deaf is urged to set up study guides and films for use in such programs.

Government Activity: For bridging gaps that now exist in services to the deaf, it is recommended that within the framework of the National Institute of Mental Health (NIMH) a division for the deaf be established, with a full-time staff to include one educator of the deaf for liaison and coordination purposes. The functions of the section could include: (1) informing schools, agencies and State mental health departments of possible funds available to them; setting up seminars for houseparents, educators, and other professional workers; setting up federal scholarships for social workers, psychiatrists, psychologists; establishing or funding training programs in colleges and universities; serving as a clearinghouse for exchange of newly researched professional data; setting up programs such as "deaf units" in state hospitals, halfway houses, and sheltered workshops; establishing guidelines for statewide planning services, etc.; conducting research (See also under Research).

It is recommended that a representative of the division for the deaf to be set up within the framework of NIMH be sent to major urban centers to meet with parents of deaf children in an ongoing program that would continue as long as the deaf child is in school. The purpose of the program would be to assist parents in understanding their children and the problems they may be having during specific phases of their development.

The Babbidge Report on the Education of the Deaf provided much valuable information with respect to existing academic and vocational programs for the deaf and made definite recommendations for needed improvements in these areas. It is recommended that the National Advisory Committee on Education of the Deaf (NACED) be encouraged to recommend to the Secretary of Health, Education, and Welfare that another national study, this time on the mental health conditions of the deaf, be undertaken at the earliest possible date.

It is recommended that the Social and Rehabilitation Service (SRS) be encouraged to give high priority to the replication of the New York State Mental Health Services demonstration in various areas of the nation.

It is recommended that SRS fund summer programs on a regional basis for the training of dormitory counselors in schools for the deaf.

It is recommended that the Office of Education, Bureau of Education for the Handicapped be urged to give high priority to proposals to investigate ways whereby the schools can best assist parents and children in the acceptance of hearing loss. The information thus obtained should then be made available to all schools serving hearing-impaired children.

It is recommended that there be a consultant on the deaf at the state level who would assist schools and other agencies to provide mental health services.

Funding by appropriate government agencies is also recommended for programs to meet the critical need of trained supervisory personnel (houseparents) in residential schools for the deaf.

Research: It is recommended that basic research be directed to learning activities in the classroom that would foster good self-concepts and self-esteem. Such activities would include successful communication, play experiences, and group activity.

Discussion Group II: Psychology

Introduction: The psychology group, in reporting their discussion of the impact of psychology on the problems of mental health of the deaf, felt that the types of problems seen could be categorized into: (1) Problems comparable to those in hearing populations, such as heightened dependency needs, impulsivity, and acting out, passive-aggressive reactions, underachievement, and parental rejection. (2) Special problems created by membership in a minority group or subculture or growing out of the relationship of such a subgroup to the majority, the non-deaf population. In the minority group or subculture are found such characteristics as isolationism, lowered expectations, inadequate identification, compensatory clannishness, and social immaturity. In the majority group, there are reactions based on stereotyped attitudes, and such unconscious reactions as rejection or indulgence. (3) Problems created by the fact of deafness itself. These effects could include such behaviors as hypersensitivity, distractibility, instability, hyperactivity, related to secondary organic defects, or cognitive and perceptual differences resulting from decreased auditory relationship with the environment. The reverberating effects of impaired or negligible communication abilities on all areas of development and achievement would also be included.

Types of Problems Seen: Among the types of problems seen are:

1. Lessened expectations for deaf children, with lessened achievement and reduced compliance with social norms. Often the child remains handicapped because of these attitudes and the parent's unconscious needs to keep him that way. This results in and is a result of over-indulgence and fostered dependency.

2. Isolation and withdrawal: because of underdeveloped verbal, motor and game skills, deaf children may not participate freely with their peers.

3. So-called "paranoid" ideas of the deaf—these may have some basis in reality—for other people do often think of them and do treat them as stupid, crazy or inferior. This may result in behaviors associated with compensatory reactions, such as pulling stunts in an attempt to prove to themselves and others that they are similar and competent.

4. Problem behaviors growing out of a parental vacuum. Such a vacuum can be made even more intense when school administrations unwittingly alienate parents, so that they fail to maintain or develop strong ties with their children in schools.

5. The so-called "institutionalized personality." This results from an overly structured school environment, submission to authority's demands for conformity, and from parent and teacher indulgence. It is evidenced by dependency, immaturity and perhaps lowered motivational levels. There are also the effects of premature "student status." Eighteen months may be too young an age to alter the usual nurturant environment by the presence of so-called "teachers," and the child may need further acceptance as he is, before attempts are made to change him. Finally there is the potential for ambivalence and confusion to be aroused by differences between home and school in their instructional and developmental expectations of the child.

Referrals: Under present conditions, most referrals are crisis oriented. The psychology group regards this type of referral as having disadvantages which should be avoided whenever possible. To this end more continuous, multidisciplinary contact with the deaf is desirable. Need was expressed for a more adequate definition of those behaviors and conditions that warrant referral of deaf children and adults. This type of information should be widely disseminated among teachers, physicians, families, and agencies serving deaf persons. There is recognition of a further need to discriminate between the difficulties of a teacher in dealing with the special problems presented by some deaf pupils, and difficulties which are the specific child's. The question to be faced is whether the "disease" is in the referral source itself, in the programming, in the child, or in a combination of these.

Management and/or Disposition: Regardless of the source of the problem or problems, what is needed in the field of psychology are specially trained people, special facilities, and special methodologies to assist those who are deaf. Psychologists' activities, besides diagnostic functions, can be directed towards: restoration of function rather than remission of symptoms; preventive goals, through studies of syndromes among the deaf, their warning signals and conditions, their process and course; promotion of positive mental health through in-service programs for teachers, parents, and members of allied professional disciplines.

Recommendations

Recommendations of the psychology group for the improvement of mental health services to the deaf come under the heading of referrals, hospitalization, personnel, parent counseling, the group approach, educational approach, and the deaf themselves.

Referrals: It is recommended that those involved with referrals of deaf people be encouraged to record and report behaviors and the situations in which they occur rather than diagnoses or judgments.

Hospitalization: With respect to hospitalization, it is recommended that regional or national facilities and programs are preferable to state-wide ones. Hospitals are to be encouraged to group inpatients together in providing therapeutic services. It is estimated that approximately 5 percent of hospitalized deaf mental patients have Usher's syndrome (congenital deafness and progressive blindness, combined with chronic brain syndromes.) Screening programs for both children and patients could lead to early diagnosis and that genetic counseling which can contribute to prevention and amelioration of this incurable double handicap.

Parent Counseling: With regard to more adequate parent counseling, it is recommended that preschool programs should not exclude deaf parents of deaf children as is now often the case. Participation of deaf parents should be encouraged in mixed groups with hearing parents, with interpreters provided if needed. (See also under The Deaf Themselves.) Preparation of the teachers of preschool deaf children should include extensive academic and practicum training in the special area of parent counseling. Provision should also be made so that social workers can also obtain this kind of training. (See also under Personnel.)

In conjunction with the current emphasis on early identification and early education of deaf children, there should be extensive parent counseling dealing specifically with psychological mechanisms related to feelings and reactions about deafness. The counseling should review the facts and ways of coping with problems of education, social adjustment, vocational planning, and the like. Parent institutes, services of mental health therapists in speech and hearing centers, special lectures, or the development of printed manuals for parents and teachers by the groups represented at this conference are among the means proposed to implement such help to parents.

Personnel: For teachers, houseparents, mental health practitioners, and other workers with deaf children it is recommended that courses in manual communication be included as part of the training. Adequate mental health information should also be put into the hands of those who train teachers of the deaf. In general, the recommendation is to increase the proficiency of those already working with the deaf rather than to proliferate more programs. This would include in teacher-training programs, sensitivity training, and more training in psychology. It is recommended that guidelines be drawn for schools with regard to appropriate ratios of pupils per psychologist, per psychiatrist, and per social worker. In this connection, it is further recommended that appropriate standards be set up and accepted for professionals in schools. Pressure is to be put on The American Psychological Association, the professional organization of psychologists, for more programs for clinical psychologists.

Group Approach: Instead of separate residential day schools for the deaf located away from population centers, it is recommended that day schools be located in central urban complexes where all types of services

—psychological, psychiatric, and social work are available for deaf children as well as for their parents. It is recommended further that cooperation rather than defensive competition be developed among those agencies and people working with the deaf. It is also recommended that people be trained to deal with a broad spectrum of factors related to deafness, rather than that they receive rigid training in a single discipline. The discussion group emphasized that behavior change in the deaf be encouraged by working with all those involved in mental health problems—parents, teachers, and counselors. It was also recommended that psychologists and social workers attending this conference use their influence to push for more psychological and social work services for the deaf by encouraging internships for psychologists and social workers in schools and other centers.

Educational Approach: It is recommended that participants in this conference encourage innovation in schools, to the end of discouraging the institutionalized personality that grows out of institutional living. Emotional education in schools and the encouragement of emotional expression in appropriate ways is as important as intellectual and technological education, and should reduce the need for "emotional re-education" or psychotherapy. More programs for the emotionally disturbed handicapped child should be developed in the form of more special facilities within the schools. Professionals in psychology should be recruited and assigned to develop a guide book for parent and teacher use for the promotion of mental health among deaf children. The discussion group also recommends the development of a central registry for bibliographies on problems related to deafness, as for example, hereditary syndromes. Finally, schools should be directed to put more emphasis on how children learn rather than how to teach; and individualized learning for each child should be the goal of every teacher.

The Deaf Themselves: The psychology group recommends making greater use of the deaf themselves. This could be done by encouraging the deaf to enter the clinical field through opening up more opportunities for them in that field. One way would be to increase the number of undergraduate and graduate programs for the deaf, and to provide more interpreters and more financial support for students. Professional people who are themselves deaf are held to be more valuable to the deaf than are hearing professionals; it is felt that the deaf will come to them more readily because of the presumption that they can better understand deafness and its problems.

Both funding and programming should be provided for both deaf and hearing persons to prepare academically and professionally for careers in mental health services with the deaf. College programs in this field as well as special institutes are suggested ways of providing such needs.

Volunteer programs of people, especially deaf people, to work with the deaf should be developed. Deaf people can also be urged to work with parents of deaf children, to provide emotional support. Further, deaf people should be selected and trained to do specialized volunteer work with the deaf, for example, in community programs that may be developed by community mental health agencies. Utilization of the deaf should include the development of career ladders so that deaf persons may move from less skilled to more skilled jobs, such as teacher aides, rehabilitation aides, counseling aides, psychological aides, community worker aides. In team approaches, the inclusion of a deaf professional is to be encouraged whenever possible. Members of the deaf community should also function as tutors for deaf children.

Miscellaneous Recommendations: It is recommended that more public relations work is needed, to overcome stereotyping of deaf people, to provide information on resources available, to inform those in power of the need for better and more adequate services, and to provide pressure to secure such services.

It is recommended that schools for the deaf be encouraged to have themselves surveyed by the Child Welfare League.

It is recommended that the New York's Mental Health Project for the Deaf should be utilized as a prototype for work with children and adults. Federal support for replication of this model should be contingent upon the provision of necessary services within the designs submitted, and regional plans should be considered.

Legislation is recommended for recording deafness in infancy.

Discussion Group III: Rehabilitation

Mental Health Problems Encountered: The rehabilitation group discussed the mental health problems they encounter and how such problems come to the attention of the rehabilitation counselor. Included are problems of social adjustment of a moderately serious nature, reflecting social immaturity and inadequacies in basic social skills. Adolescent problems, especially of the 17-21 year-old age group coming out of schools, were also considered, running the gamut from mild character disorders to unsocialized and incorrigible individuals. Other categories were problems of marital relationship and of sexual confusion, and problems relating to sensory deprivation and the language gap, reflected in a variety of symptoms such as isolation, withdrawal, feelings of persecution, etc. Also discussed were the problems of the deaf person returning to the community from mental hospitals and/or correctional systems, and the many job-adjustment problems of deaf clients that the vocational rehabilitation counselor encounters, which have multiple causes related to mental health.

Sources of referrals or contacts with these problems were listed as including schools for the deaf, welfare departments, juvenile courts, the deaf community, employment services, parents of deaf children, and state hospitals. It was noted that both day and residential schools do not adequately refer those clients in need of mental health aid to the Division of Vocational Guidance.

The deaf community and its acceptance and understanding of mental health services came up for considerable discussion. One facility reported a shortage of referrals and believes this to be due to denial of their needs on the part of the deaf.

Meeting the Mental Health Problems of the Deaf: It was generally felt that relatively little has been done to meet the mental health problems of the deaf. There was general agreement that the role of the vocational rehabilitation counselor is a key one because of his contacts with the members of this special population. He is looked upon as the instigator, innovator, prime mover, and cultivator of services for the deaf.

The group noted that a number of approaches have been used to deal with the need for mental health services. These vary largely on the basis of population concentrations. Some rural states utilize interpreter services to bridge the gap between client and service. Larger cities, New York and Chicago, for example, have both inpatient and outpatient facilities staffed by persons able to communicate with the deaf. The State of Texas has used an active volunteer program to initiate services to the deaf through its state hospital system. Illinois, through a separate funding source, is able within the Vocational Rehabilitation program to purchase additional casework services, interpreters, etc., for greater in-depth counseling than would otherwise be available. Michigan has a residential program for children offering direct services to them; consultation in this state is being offered to the houseparent staff of the state's residential school, and current plans call for moving a psychiatric unit to the campus of the school for the deaf.

On the theory that mental health is enhanced by good employment adjustment, Illinois plans to set up a summer program for deaf students in the 9th-12th grade category. The program will have a two-fold goal: to teach sign language to day-school children who need it, and to expand vocational preparation and knowledge through a combination of lectures and on-the-job experience.

Elsewhere, a number of rehabilitation programs are actively working with the deaf community to educate them regarding mental health needs, and to solicit their active participation in securing better services for the deaf.

Coordinating Rehabilitation Efforts with those of Other Groups: The discussion group held that not much has as yet been done in coordinating rehabilitation efforts with other groups. It strongly supported a team approach to the multiple needs of the deaf. The group agreed that rehabilitation has responsibility, not only for suitable referral, but also for follow-up, once services are provided.

The role which state vocational rehabilitation agencies can take with the younger deaf child was brought up. Some discussants felt that those who direct planning at the Federal level are beginning to see rehabilitation as a cradle-to-grave concept. Workers in contact with the deaf were strongly urged not to wait until the client had already been "fouled up." On the contrary, it was urged, clients should be reached early when services could still be preventive.

Both the present meeting and the recent workshop at Las Cruces were viewed by the group as a positive step in the direction of improved interagency communication and cooperation. The desire was expressed to see in the near future similar cooperative gatherings on both state and local levels among educators, mental health people, and Rehabilitation Service agencies.

Rehabilitation personnel were encouraged to participate actively on key lay committees which present significant recommendations to legislatures. They were reminded that the deaf community constitutes a body of voters and that their united influence can be enlisted to move government to provide programming.

A cardinal point, repeatedly emphasized, was how important it is for rehabilitation personnel to have frequent contact with the deaf community in order to keep tuned in to their needs, and to be able to assist the deaf community to take a greater leadership role in securing mental health services for the deaf.

Limitations on Present Rehabilitation Efforts: In discussing limitations on present rehabilitation efforts, the group took up problems currently being met in attempting to provide services.

Referral problems were mentioned. Even among rehabilitation people, there is not always agreement on just what constitutes a mental health problem. The lack of understanding of mental health problems that exist today among the deaf was also emphasized. Some vocational rehabilitation counselors were held to be uncertain as to the limitations of vocational rehabilitation counseling and just when it is indicated that other disciplines with more specialized training should be called on. Interagency weaknesses were admitted to exist specifically in the lack of communication between disciplines. As demonstrated in this conference, there is a great deal that one discipline can learn from other disciplines in the overall concept of rehabilitation.

Then, too, gaps exist in client readiness for service and in the availability of services. Sometimes, for example, rehabilitation workers do not know if they can service children or the severely disturbed because of administrative pressures, uncertainties, and emphasis upon case closure. At the heart of many problems is the external communication barrier with all its implications. The lack of knowledge, on the part of the hearing population, of the specific problems of the deaf suggests an ever-increasing demand for educational approaches that will make those who are able to provide mental health services, aware of the deaf and of their needs.

Recommendations

Recommendations in the Rehabilitation field were grouped under counseling, the deaf themselves, and government activity.

Counseling: With respect to rehabilitation counseling for the deaf, it is recommended that special orientation be provided as part of the ongoing training for rehabilitation counselors of the deaf, so that in their work with mental health problems of the deaf they will be better prepared to recognize mental health problems and to take appropriate steps. Programs such as the one at New York could provide excellent learning experience for rehabilitation counselors. Also, it is recommended that rehabilitation counselors be made an integral part of the educational team in residential schools for the deaf and be drawn in at the earliest possible time, as personnel become available. A further recommendation is that every effort should be made to explore how existing mental health facilities might be utilized and incorporated into the vocational rehabilitation program of services to the deaf. It is recommended, also, that each rehabilitation counselor should familiarize himself with his local state laws regarding commitment procedures so that he will be able to deal promptly and adequately with those who are suffering from acute mental health problems of an emergency nature.

It is further recommended that experienced counselors of the deaf be allowed to serve more as coordinators, and to devote more time to developing good community services and facilities. It was suggested that they oversee the progress of such efforts, and fully utilize and pay for community resources such as deaf leaders and interpreters on a consultative basis to do the leg work, communication, and other necessary but not too demanding duties. It was urged that less attention be paid to closure of cases and greater emphasis be placed on solutions to the mental health problems of the deaf.

With respect to the rehabilitation counselor's contribution to prevention it is recommended that recognition be given to careful and conscientious placement of the deaf rehabilitation client as a preventive approach to mental health problems. Poor placement can create mental health problems if social and deaf community factors are not recognized and given careful consideration. Recommendations also include that schools for the deaf be encouraged to have available to them mental health team consultation for purposes of (1) in-service training of school personnel, (2) early evaluation of children, and (3) on-going follow-up of a child's progress with an eye to having such a consultative service serve as a preventive measure.

The Deaf Themselves: With respect to the deaf themselves, it is recommended by the vocational rehabilitation group that the deaf be encouraged to carry on their persons identification cards containing their name and an interpreter's name and how the latter might be reached in an emergency. Another recommendation is that the Registry of Interpreters for the Deaf continue to develop means by which interpreters can be specifically trained and certified to work in mental health settings. It was suggested that the telephone answering services of Kansas City and Pittsburgh could serve as guidelines for possible development of such emergency contact services in other metropolitan areas. In both cities an agreement has been reached between community interpreters and the agency on the organization of voluntary interpreter services. Interpreters are assigned specific days and hours on the basis of their availability. Their schedule is in the hands of the agency person responsible for services to the deaf. During office hours any deaf person in need of an interpreter can call directly to the agency to make the necessary arrangements for interpreter services. After hours, an answering service is used; the deaf in need of an interpreter calls the answering service and leaves his address or phone number; the service forwards this information hourly either to the interpreter directly or to the agency person. Prompt response is then made to the request.

It is further recommended that there be a continued development, both through Captioned Films and other appropriate cooperating sources, of films, plays, and other visual-aid materials to educate the deaf population about mental health principles. The development of speech correction programs for deaf adults (not necessarily the orally trained deaf) is recommended as a measure of promoting more participation in community activities by the deaf leadership.

It is recommended also that workshops for the deaf community be encouraged to orient them to existing services in their community and how best they might use such services.

Government Activity: With respect to government activity in the field of mental health services for the deaf, it is recommended that mental health authorities in each state be asked to make a survey of mental health facilities to determine how many deaf are currently confined in state hospitals and how many are being serviced on an outpatient basis. It is also recommended that the Social and Rehabilitation Service (SRS) or other appropriate agency be established as an informational clearing house for hospitals and other mental health facilities that would secure and distribute information and guidelines from already established programs in order to assist states in developing programs of their own. SRS could also disseminate this information through the regional offices to the "grass roots" counselor. Specific information regarding referral procedures, costs, type of client serviced, etc., should be included so that the wisest use could be made of existing facilities.

It is further recommended that additional regional centers be established to serve those deaf persons with personal adjustment problems from populations with a low density of deaf people. Such facilities cannot now be justified on a local basis for small numbers. Another recommendation is that encouragement and support be given by SRS to regional and local workshops to bring together the disciplines of education, rehabilitation, and mental health, and that every effort be made by SRS to encourage greater coordination between rehabilitation and the National Institute of Mental Health. It was also recommended that NIMH be sought as a source of funds for program development in mental health services to the deaf.

Discussion Group IV: Religion

Introduction: While they are not generally the first group to make contact with the troubled deaf person, the clergy does have a role to play in the mental health of the deaf. The discussion among the clerical group emphasized that they are only slowly beginning to become aware of this responsibility.

In most cases, the parents of a deaf child first contact the medical profession. The physician, diagnosing the child that is not responding to his auditory environment as do other children of his age, may or may not turn to other specialists. In any event, he is the one that takes on the medical management of the child and that advises the parents. And he may make erroneous statements as to the prognosis for the child and his vocational potential. Occasionally, mistakes are in the direction of undue pessimism, e.g., "the child is mentally retarded"; more commonly, however, through either misunderstanding or misplaced sympathy, false hopes are held out to the parents.

The Problems and How They Are Handled: The initial diagnosis often gives rise to a traumatic experience that touches upon the religious value system of many parents. They then turn to the clergy for spiritual advice and guidance. This is apt to be the first point at which clergymen come in contact with the deaf. If they are unfamiliar with the problem of deafness in children, they may be guilty as some medical men in giving erroneous advice about the child's future. They may lose sight of the opportunity they have for helping the mental health of the child through their role in the spiritual counseling of the child's parents. It is generally believed that the later emotional problems of deaf children and adults have their origin in the emotional problems of parents who, having been poorly counseled, have never been helped to accept the reality of their situation and that of their children.

Such a parent often confronts his clergymen with the question: Why should God do this to me? Involved in a query of this kind is the whole matter of the presence of evil in the world. Parents may come to look upon their God as a God of vengeance and, thinking of themselves as being punished for some past sin or sins, they may develop feelings of persecution. It is to be emphasized that such feelings of guilt are an emotional problem, and are to be distinguished from the theological

136

concept of guilt, a guilt to be absolved by God's goodness and forgiveness. Bitterness towards God in the hearts of some parents can become expressed or reflected in a rejection of the child, with serious deleterious effect on the child's mental health.

Some hearing parents, failing to understand the child's need for their love, make every effort to have someone else take the deaf child off their hands. Others, uncomprehending of the true meaning of love, may react to their inner guilt feelings by becoming overprotective and overpossessive of their child. Still others look for a miracle, rather than striving to change their own attitudes and to accept the reality. The wish may express itself in a constant search for someone who will finally tell them that the child is not handicapped and will be "all right." As a consequence, these misguided parents are found traveling from one doctor to another, from one center to another, from one clinic to another, hoping and praying for the wished-for response. Thus they never face up to the real situation. The clergy must be careful not to encourage such self-delusion. Furthermore, the clergy must understand the pressures and tensions that can arise in a marriage as a result of the presence of a deaf child. If they feel that they are not competent to handle the deep spiritual and other complex problems often having serious emotional overtones, they should seek out competent fellow clergymen who know about deafness and who have had experience in counseling such parents. These men know their limitations as clergymen, and will refer those parents who are seriously emotionally disturbed to other professionals properly equipped to handle the clinical problems involved.

A further problem faces the clergyman who does refer such problems to a psychiatrist or psychologist in that the professional must be well informed on the specific problems of the deaf. The group made note of one situation where a psychiatrist, fully competent in the general field of psychiatry but without specific experience or knowledge of the deaf, consulted with a deaf adult; he diagnosed the patient's problem correctly as one of overdependence upon his mother, but advised the patient to make his own telephone calls instead of relying on his mother as he had for years. This reliance was, in fact, a part of the dependency syndrome, but the area chosen in which to alter behavior would never have been selected by someone familiar with the deaf.

Work with the parents of the deaf child, whether by the clergy or by others, was looked upon by the group as a preventive measure to insure the mental health of the deaf child. Problems of deaf parents and their hearing children, and of hearing parents and their deaf children were discussed. It was pointed out that some hearing children were ashamed before others, of their deaf parents; on the other hand, cultural aspects of a hearing child's life may be unappreciated by the deaf parents (e.g., a child's desire to take music lessons), a situation that could lead to friction between parents and child. Other problems would be common regardless of whether the combination was hearing parents and deaf child or deaf parents and hearing child. These include

138 MENTAL HEALTH AND THE DEAF: APPROACHES AND PROSPECTS

difficulties in providing adequate parental counseling about dating, marriage, and the like, where parents might not be able to explain things satisfactorily to their children; guidance about the child's use of improper language (which the parents either could not see or could not hear); or even disruption of such normal parent-child activities as assisting with homework. The danger of precocity for hearing children was discussed, when the children are compelled to act as interpreters in the handling of their deaf parents' problems. The whole range of problems are multiplied and intensified when they concern relationships of hearing parents with a deaf child and with his hearing siblings; or those of a hearing parent married to a deaf parent, in the matter of identifying with a hearing child or a deaf child; or the dynamics of the family constellation when younger hearing siblings are given greater responsibilities (and perhaps greater privileges) than their older deaf brothers and sisters.

The discussion emphasized equally the role of the clergy with deaf adults having emotional problems, and with the community resources that are—or that should be—available to assist in the immediate amelioration of such problems. The clergy also felt the challenge to them to recruit and educate their own group and others in the consideration of these dynamics as they affect the individual, his family, and their mental health.

Gaps in Service: Many communities through the country were found not to have any resources that the clergy can call on to assist them in meeting the mental health needs of their deaf parishoners. Where resources are available, there are often no personnel who know sign language or who are interested in learning it so that they might help the deaf. In short, there is virtually a total absence of resources with both awareness and understanding of the deaf as a subcultural group. Moreover, in some cases where the clergy had tried to enlist the services of outside professionals, there appeared to be some unexplained fear or embarrassment about handling such cases, and as a result the situations were too frequently avoided.

The clergy felt that they as a profession needed to gain greater insight into the area of emotional disorders, so that they would be enabled to judge when a problem was no longer amenable to spiritual direction and guidance but required clinical therapeutic service.

Recommendations

The discussion group made a number of suggestions and recommendations which fell into two groups: (1) What the clergy themselves can do to meet the mental health needs of the deaf, both children and adults; (2) What the clergy can do to interest others in the mental health problems of the deaf.

What the Clergy Can Do: Clergymen should contact local resources and offer to participate in ongoing educational and service programs for the deaf. They should seek assistance from existing state agencies to set up such programs where they are not now in existence. They can and should alert community mental health centers funded by the government to the problems involving the deaf. Within their various denominations they should encourage (a) support for special training for their clergy in the areas of mental health generally and especially in these problems as they exist among the deaf; the latter should be obtained under a knowledgeable staff, trained and experienced in care of the deaf, and (b) support for increased numbers of clergymen once they are thus trained.

The clergy can also institute and contribute to the development of better programs in parent education. They can supply chaplains or a list of available clergy to diagnostic centers and to preschool programs, to work with the spiritual aspects of parents' problems while professional personnel work simultaneously with the clinical aspects.

Furthermore, the clergy should work toward securing the support of the Department of Health, Education, and Welfare for one or more graduate training centers where clergymen could be trained in the competencies needed for work with the deaf. Their efforts should also be brought to bear on the establishment of a pastoral-clinical training center for training pastoral counselors for work with the deaf. They should work closely for and with halfway house programs for deaf people who are not yet able to live independently or in family situations, and in this capacity strive to meet the spiritual needs of the residents of such halfway houses.

The clergy should also, where feasible, enlist the deaf themselves in information programs for the deaf and for professionals.

What the Clergy Can Do to Interest Others: The clergy should try to reach professionals by submitting articles for their professional publications and by lectures before professional groups. They can invite professionals to the institutions for the deaf with which they are connected, so that these professionals can have personal contact with the deaf and their problems. They can reach the parents of deaf children through printed material in the religious press, for wide distribution through centers where the deaf parents congregate.

Discussion Group V: Social Work

Introduction: The role of the social worker with deaf children and adults was prominent in the discussions of the group. Though at present very few professionally trained social workers are working with the deaf, there was no disagreement about the fact that professionally trained social workers should be an essential part of any team working to bring deaf persons of all ages to the full realization of their potential.

It was noted that schools for the deaf too often have untrained houseparents, teachers lacking in knowledge and awareness of emotional illness, a lack of clinical professionals on their staff, school policies which do not relate to social work, and social workers limited to work with parents—a situation which prevents the deaf child from achieving his best possible level of social function. Noted also was the lack of communication *with* parents, and the lack of communication *from* parents which results in a deaf child's being deprived of the normal stimulus and interest given by average parents to their hearing children.

The discussion referred to the basic fact that social work is concerned with the process of the person's total socialization within the total community. In this respect social work is unique, functioning as it does somewhat independently of other disciplines. The social worker is a professional with a complete knowledge of community resources available, an understanding of the environment and of a person's reactions to stress and the world around him. Thus the social worker is especially qualified to work in the area of maturational processes.

Social workers functioning in a team for deaf children or adults could be used as consultants to teachers, as well as to lay persons working with the deaf. They could provide an insight into deaf people's social difficulties. They could help the deaf school graduates make the transition from school life to life in a world that is far less structured, and far less protective. In hearing and speech centers the social worker could be a valuable aid, relieving the speech therapist of the task—often assumed out of necessity—of trying to help parents with their feelings about their child

140

and his deafness, or adults and their feelings about having become deaf.

The social work group also felt that social workers could be used by schools as directors of cottage life. In this context they would have the responsibility for training houseparents, and for coordinating the total environment of the children so that there would be smoother movement in the direction of total maturation.

Mental Health Problems Encountered: Social workers, being particularly interested in each person's realization of his full potential within the culture and society, are especially sensitive to various problems in social functioning which may be traced to deafness. Summarizing their viewpoint, the group felt that deafness produces a condition where the total maturational process is out of kilter because of a thwarted input. Resulting symptoms may be described as naivete, impulsivity, action based on pleasure gratification, difficulty with identification, and self-isolation.

Social workers have contact with deaf people whose language skills are limited and who may be without efficient communication skills despite their years. There appears to be a psychosocial lag among deaf persons, linked with the handicap itself; thus the deaf in society are underdeveloped or lag behind the rest of the community and the culture. It was brought out in the discussion that the deaf person is often fearful of the world and resists efforts to lead him into an unsheltered life. An important aspect of the problem is that deaf persons often have experiences of a social nature that they do not understand and that are not explained to them. With a proper explanation, the deaf person could more readily understand the experience and grow from it. Often, too, deaf people have problems growing out of non-acceptance by their neighbors and peers in the hearing community. Further, many deaf persons are frustrated because of the expectancy placed upon them for adequate oral communication performance, which few are able to fulfill.

How Social Workers Learn of These Problems: Unlike some other professionals helping the deaf, social workers rarely see the deaf adult first. Rehabilitation workers, old teachers, friends, or to a lesser extent, ministers, are often the first to whom the grown deaf person comes with a problem. In other words, social work is not conceived of naturally by the deaf person as a method of helping people. The hearing community, generally, has arrived at a point where it takes advantage of the help available through social work agencies—but the social lag and limited awareness of the deaf is such that they do not yet see such agencies as places where they can get help.

Accordingly, deaf persons who do see social workers are mainly referred to them by others. The referral will generally be made by a minister or rehabilitation counselor, for example, with the thought of trying to help the person to improve his social functioning. Only in those schools for the deaf where professionally trained social workers are on the staff and working directly with the children—and such schools are few and far between—will the social worker be thought of frequently as the first person to be contacted when problems arise.

What Has Been Done to Date: The group drew a negative rather than a positive picture of the past and present situation. Social work as a profession has been neglected in many agencies established to help and educate the deaf. Too often, speech and hearing centers rely instead on their speech therapists to handle the emotional problems of clients and their parents.

The consensus was also that in the very few schools for the deaf that do have social workers the work was often *around* the students rather than *with* them. Many of these workers are without professional training, and they are mainly utilized to help parents fill out forms rather than being considered a resource to the school for helping students.

The further point was made that even those social workers who are called upon to work with the deaf do not generally have the necessary skill in communication to do the work properly. Thus the worker tends toward turning to the environment around the deaf person rather than directly to the person himself. Feeling the limitations in help when communication is adequate, the deaf client tends to drop out, thereby adding to the vicious cycle.

Attempts to Work Together with Other Groups: Among the group there was considerable difference of opinion as to what social workers should do and the role they should play. The differences obtained among social workers themselves and between the workers and resource personnel from other disciplines. The evidence indicated that the profession of social work had not succeeded in interpreting its function to other professions nor to the deaf community, aggravating the prevalence of disuse and misuse of social work.

It was brought out also that some of the professional disciplines with a long-established tradition of work with the deaf may have difficulty in giving up some or any of what they feel is their rightful historic role. This may contribute to the situation already noted where, even today, most schools for the deaf do not have social workers on their staff. The misconception held to is that "understanding" teachers are all that are required to help students with their problems. Truly, many people may obtain satisfaction from helping people with problems, and may not be eager to relinquish that aspect of their work. However, it was held that it is to the deaf person's benefit to enlist the kind of cooperation in which speech therapist and teacher are each free to do his special work, together with a social worker who is also enabled to do his part.

The picture of the social worker as no more than a "do-gooder" was held to be regrettable. Such a view, it was felt, underrates the profession and its method, and hampers the real and valuable work that can be done. A necessary key to cooperation is correct understanding of and respect for the professional social worker. With teammates not understanding the position, responsibility and potential value of their teammates, there are bound to be collisions!

Recommendations

Here again, the recommendations embraced the fields of training, personnel, the deaf themselves and government activity.

Training: It is recommended that programs of social work education explore the possibility of establishing within social work schools new programs in which people can be trained to work specifically with the deaf, and of offering field work placements for students interested in such work. These placements should emphasize the communication skills necessary for the worker with the deaf.

Further, it is recommended that university training programs already offering courses in connection with the deaf should open their orientation and training programs to students and specialists in social work training. Other universities should be encouraged to initiate similar programs.

It is recommended that every effort should be made to inform the proper committees of the National Association of Social Workers (NASW) of the tremendous need in the area of social work service for the deaf, and that NASW be encouraged to cooperate in efforts to establish more programs for training workers for the deaf.

It is recommended that groups working with the deaf should contact local social work agencies and encourage their staffs to acquire communication skills and knowledge of the concepts of deafness, so that they might increase their usefulness in this important field.

Personnel: It is recommended that every effort be made to utilize and include social workers in programs offering education and rehabilitation to the deaf person, as well as in other settings where deaf people need help, even where the social workers have to work through interpreters. Social workers should be used in giving direct service to clients and also in instructing and helping other personnel to understand the needs and problems of deaf people. They should be called in when the diagnosis of deafness is made, when treatment in clinic or school begins, at the end of the treatment program, and at the transition from school to life in the outside world.

It is finally recommended that each community should establish a referral service that is knowledgeable in local services for the deaf. This service agency should also attempt to stimulate local social and case work agencies to make their services available to deaf people.

The Deaf Themselves: It is recommended that undergraduate programs for the deaf should encourage able deaf students to enter graduate schools of social work and the Gallaudet College should be encouraged to offer courses in pre-social work. The latter courses should be given recognition by regular graduate schools of social work to which a deaf student may transfer upon graduation from Gallaudet.

Government Activity: Programs providing necessary financial support for students entering the graduate social work training should be developed and funded.

It is also recommended that study should be made of the present situation in connection with the number of social workers serving the deaf and in what institutions they are active, so that authoritative and specific recommendations can be made to the Department of Health, Education, and Welfare to stimulate the development of services in this area.

A.
Organization of the Conference

PLANNING COMMITTEE

Rainer, J. D., *Chairman*
Altshuler, K. Z., *Co-Chairman and Editor*
Wiggam, E., *Administrator*
Hoemann, H. W.
Reed, L. D.

Stelle, R.
Tully, N.
Vernon, M.
Williams, B.
Woodrick, W.

Newcomb, W., *Coordinator*
Cataldo, M., *Administrative Assistant*

RESOURCE PERSONNEL

Brown, D.
Burke, D.
Galloway, V. H.
Hourihan, J. P.

Hurwitz, S.
Krug, R. F.
McClure, W. J.
Rosenstein, J.

INTERPRETERS

Abbott, L.
Beard, L.
Duncan, J.
Holland, B.
Hughes, V.

Johnson, S. D.
Kleeb, R.
Lewis, V.
Pacetti, S.
Shipman, J. S.

Hoemann, H. W., *Chief*

DISCUSSION GROUP I: EDUCATION

Hoffmeyer, B. E., *Chairman*
Youngs, J. P., *Recorder*
Babb, R.
Berke, A.
Blea, W.
Dillon, T.
Farman, J. J.
Fein, J.
Giangreco, C. J.
Graham, J. K.
Kent, M. S.
Lane, K. R.

McClure, W. J.
Northcott, W.
O'Rourke, T.
Phillips, R.
Rose, E. F.
Roth, S.
Scouten, E. L.
Stelle, R.
Tully, N.
Turechek, A. G.
Vollenweider, J. A.
Wahl, L. B.

145

DISCUSSION GROUP II: PSYCHOLOGY

Weckler, N., *Chairman*
Hess, D. W., *Recorder*
Abdullah, S.
Altshuler, K. Z.
Babbini, B.
Brenner, L.
Brown, D.
Collins, J. L.
Darnell, W.
Edelin, P.
Falberg, R.
Hancock, B. J.
Koch, H.
Krug, R. F.

Lavos, G.
Lipsett, L.
Marsters, P.
Meadow, K. P.
Naiman, D.
Pimentel, A. T.
Rollins, G. W.
Ross, D.
Stansbury, E.
Sutton, B.
Thompson, R. E.
Vernon, M.
Zabell, E. M.

DISCUSSION GROUP III: REHABILITATION

Johnson, R. K., *Chairman*
Hanson, J., *Recorder*
Benowitz, S.
Burke, D.
DiFrancesca, S.
Dow, P.
Ethridge, W. A.
Galloway, V. H.
Gattas, F.
Goetzinger, C. P.
Hawkins, R. D.
Irgens, H.

Joosten, G.
Kerr, P. A.
Lauritsen, R.
Millard, R.
Myers, D.
Pettingill, D. G.
Sanderson, R.
Skinner, R.
Sonnega, J. A.
Stewart, L. G.
Whitworth, J. H.
Woodrick, W.

DISCUSSION GROUP IV: RELIGION

Hourihan, J. P., *Chairman*
Riekehof, L., *Recorder*
Bearden, C.
Douglas, A.
Foxwell, L.
Harte, T. J.
Hoemann, H. W.
Hoffman, L.
Holdt, B. J.
Kopp, H. G.
Lange, W. M.
McVicker, E.
Morgan, D.

Newcomb, W.
Pickering, R.
Robinson, L.
Rohe, H. W.
Rosenstein, J.
Schlesinger, H.
Simonson, S.
Slasor, D.
Smucker, J. R.
Stuckless, E. R.
Willard, C.
Williams, B. R.